WINNERS!

The Story of Alcohol And Drug-Abuse Programs In the Horse Racing Industry

Curtis L. Barrett, Ph. D.
and
Don C. Clippinger

Published by

Daily Racing Form Press
10 Lake Drive
Hightstown, N.J. 08520

Cover design by Chris Donofry
Cover photo by Suzie Picou-Oldham
ISBN 0-9648493-5-6
Printed in the United States of America

Contents

Chapter 1
Billy, Doug, and Slew 1

Chapter 2
Enemies of the People 22

Chapter 3
A Strange and Seductive World 35

Chapter 4
East Side, West Side 51

Chapter 5
Silent No More 62

Chapter 6
A Standard of Excellence 71

Chapter 7
In the Shedrow and on the Farm 84

Chapter 8
Backstretch Pioneers 102

Chapter 9
My Old Kentucky Home 113

Chapter 10
The Whole Person 129

Chapter 11
The Cop and the Jock 136

Chapter 12
The Chaplaincy: In a Place with No Name . . 149

Chapter 13
America's Fastest Athlete 159

Chapter 14
What if We Do Nothing 171

Chapter 15
Epilogue 181

Dedication

My portion of Winners! is dedicated to my wife Jane, whose time for companionship I have given, over the past decade, to the horse racing industry, to conferences, and to this book. On a racetrack somewhere is an addict – now safe, clean and sober – who should be as grateful to Jane for his sober life as I am grateful to her for mine.

C.B.

For my parts of this book, I am greatly indebted to two people: my wife, Audrey Korotkin, and J. Terrence Carson, of blessed memory. Audrey, always my inspiration, attended all of the Louisville sessions of the Conference on Alcohol and Drug Abuse Programs for the Horse Racing Industry and provided wise counsel on this work at crucial times.

Terry Carson, the best brother this only child ever had, knew a lot about drinking, and in the last quarter century of his life knew even more about sobriety. In Pittsburgh, his hometown, he helped hundreds, if not thousands, to a new life through 12-step recovery. Terry read drafts of several Winners! chapters and at one point said: "Somebody is going to read this and get sober." I can only pray that he was right. I dedicate my part of this book to Terry's memory.

D.C.

Foreword

The addicted life is a sinkhole of despair, and the greatest gift for those afflicted is hope.

Hope is the message of this book, a message projected loudly through its pages. The messengers are not only the authors, Curt Barrett and Don Clippinger, although they speak clearly in these chapters. The drunks and druggies who find a way out; the chaplains who minister to the souls; the racetrackers who refuse to enable; the executives who make help freely available – they also carry the message of hope to all who suffer.

There is a turning point for every addict where a push one way or the other will make all the difference between drowning in a sea of drugs and alcohol, or latching onto the life preserver of recovery. The stories in this book could provide a push in the right direction.

Winners! is a conduit, with every word passing on the experience, strength and hope of all those who contibuted to its creation. If just one word reaches its mark, if just one sentence opens the door to recovery for just one person, this book will have achieved its true purpose.

Here's hoping.

George Bernet
Hightstown, N.J.
1997

Acknowledgements

We would be remiss if we did not jointly acknowledge the contributions of time, effort, resources and financial assistance that made publication of this work possible. *Daily Racing Form* president William J. Dow assured that Winners! would see the light of day, and *Daily Racing Form* editor George J. Bernet III contributed both his talents and time to this project. Thoroughbred Racing Associations, through the efforts of executive vice president Christopher N. Scherf, provided financial support that made possible publication of this book in hard cover.

Also, those mentioned in this book, and those whom space did not allow us to mention or quote, are acknowledged here for their contributions to the Louisville conferences that provided the database for Winners! Sustaining the conferences was Dr. Robert Lawrence, director of the University of Louisville's equine administration program, with ever-present encouragement and crucial financial support. All who read Winners! should know, however, that it was the steadfast dedication and attention to detail of Gerald Swim, director of continuing education for the University of Louisville Medical School, that turned conference ideas into a memorable reality for all of those who attended the Louisville conferences.

All have won, so all shall have prizes.

C.B. & D.C.

Chapter 1

Billy, Doug, and Slew

They were so different and yet so very much alike. One, a tall and slim Easterner, emerged from the privileged world of fox hunting and steeplechase racing. The other, a tall, strongly built product of America's West, left home at age 14 to answer the siren call of the race track.

So different in their backgrounds, William H. Turner Jr. and Douglas R. Peterson shared a common bond like no other. Seattle Slew, one of the most gifted horses ever to seize the bit and race the wind, blossomed and matured in the hands of these horse people – both of whom possessed talents well beyond their years. Power, grace, and a primal ferocity bundled in a dark, sinewy half-ton of horseflesh, Slew was everything that the Thoroughbred was meant to be, and more.

With incredible speed and a will to win that accepted no barriers, Seattle Slew defied all of the odds. He won America's Triple Crown, completing his quicksilver charge through the 1977 Kentucky Derby, the Preakness Stakes, and the Belmont Stakes without a single defeat on his record. No horse had ever done that before Seattle Slew, and none has done it since his magical five-week dance through the series that, to this day, defines the finest athletes in the Thoroughbred sport.

As a four-year-old in 1978, Seattle Slew handily defeated that year's Triple Crown winner, Affirmed, and came within a few inches of claiming another triple crown, Belmont Park's handicap championship comprising the Marlboro Stakes, Woodward Stakes, and the Jockey Club Gold Cup.

For the thousands of people who occupy America's race tracks, the dream of being around a horse like Seattle Slew rolls them out of bed well before dawn every day and impels them to turn their backs on more profitable pursuits for the dirty drudgery of caring for race horses. To be sure, they love the horses, but the dream keeps them going through the bone-chilling mornings of February and the sweltering afternoons of July. Okay, they say, this bunch of horses may not be worth much, but they will sustain me until that next crop or that next sale. Then maybe – just maybe – a van will pull up to my barn with the next Slew. Their dream is illogical and probably impossible, but it stokes the fire of their existence – day by day, week by week, year by year.

For a trainer, a horse like Slew is the ultimate gift. Billy Turner and Doug Peterson were given that gift, and no one can, in the clarity of almost two decades, seriously question their stewardship. They navigated through a mine field of pressures, arising both from Slew's owners and the crush of media that surrounds a legendary race horse, and they delivered a three-time champion – North America's Horse of the Year in 1977 and probably deserving the sport's ultimate accolade in 1978 – and a horse that went on to an outstanding career at stud.

Billy Turner had Slew practically from the moment he left the Fasig-Tipton sale ring in 1975 (purchased for an incredibly inexpensive $17,500 by the partnership of Mickey and Karen Taylor and Dr. Jim and Sally Hill) until he and the remainder of their horses were yanked away under the cover of darkness in November 1977.

Doug Peterson, thrust into the presence of greatness at the age of 26, nursed Slew through illness that first winter, through minor injury that summer, and through the pressure cooker of the Belmont fall handicap series to a final victory and a triumphal retirement to Spendthrift Farm in Kentucky. After Spendthrift's collapse, Seattle Slew continued an outstanding career as a stallion at Three Chimneys Farm in Kentucky.

Yes, Billy Turner and Doug Peterson shared the ultimate experience of training Seattle Slew. But they also have something else in common – another way in which they are so much alike. They are both alcoholics. In the argot of Alcoholics Anonymous, which never has wasted time or words on euphemisms, they were drunks.

Both were active alcoholics while they were training Seattle Slew; both were drunks many, many years before Seattle Slew came into their lives. In the years after Seattle Slew, the disease known as alcoholism devoured their fortunes, devoured their dignity, devoured their talents, devoured their desire to train horses, devoured their health, and devoured their will to live.

That they are alive today is testimony only to the strength and subtlety of the liquids both of them poured down their throats. In their own ways, both tried to end their lives – to put an end to the pain and the degradation that their particular demon had caused them. They could not even get that right. Fortunately, in the end, the alcohol had robbed them even of the ability to take their own lives.

If two fine horse people such as Billy Turner and Doug Peterson can be victimized by the ravages of alcoholism, it should come as no surprise that the disease is prevalent – indeed, some say rampant – on America's race tracks. They had breathed the rarefied air at the summit of the sport, and they nonetheless were afflicted by this progressive and fatal disease. It is no wonder, then, that thousands of others, who share the dream but not the reality of the big horse, also fall victim to the disease and its impairments.

But theirs is not a tale of defeat, or even a cautionary tale against the dangers of alcohol. No, the experiences of Billy and Doug are stories of triumph. Billy Turner and Doug Peterson are sober and leading full and productive lives. At the last moment, just as alcoholism was about to snuff out their lives on its own timetable, they received a helping hand – in Turner's case, from friends and family, and from a race track assistance program for Peterson.

They surrendered to the disease that – no matter how strong and independent they thought they were – they could not beat by themselves, and they started on that long, tortuous road to recovery. Today, they are recovering alcoholics, two of the millions of Americans who realize that they have an incurable disease but overcome it day by day through their sobriety. They chose life, and they are winning their personal battles against alcoholism – one day at a time. These are the stories of two winners – Billy and Doug – who are again winning on the race track and winning at life.

BILLY'S STORY

July 5, 1991 will forever be meaningful in the life of William Hutt "Billy" Turner Jr. That was the day his now-former wife, Barbara, called two friends from Turner's steeplechasing days and said: "I think Billy's dying." And he was. That was also the day, doctors told him later, that he died. "They thought I wasn't going to make it," Turner said.

It was also the day that Billy Turner began a new life. He had very nearly ended his life by effectively committing suicide; he had stopped eating and was drinking constantly, well on his way to a fatal overdose. But, with the help of his wife, two friends, and Father Martin's Ashley in Maryland, Billy Turner's life was saved.

That dark day for Billy Turner, when he lay nearly lifeless on the backseat of a friend's car during the trek from Long Island to Maryland, was a long way from the glory days of Seattle Slew. And, it was even farther from Turner's youth, which in many ways was an ideal preparation for a champion like Seattle Slew.

Born in Rochester, New York, in 1940, Turner was the son of a Du Pont Company executive who was transferred to the giant corporation's headquarters city, Wilmington, Delaware. Billy grew up in the portion of Pennsylvania near Wilmington that includes the Philadelphia region's fox-hunting country.

It is countryside that even today, when late fall throws its gray cloak over a chill landscape and renders morning indistinguishable from afternoon, is reminiscent of England's hunting fields. Then and now, horses and hounds run for miles and miles over the undulating Pennsylvania landscape in pursuit of the fox.

For some, mostly the rich and privileged, the fox hunting defines their lives, and Turner – although not of that economic class – learned his horsemanship in the heart of Pennsylvania's fox-hunting country, Mr. Stewart's Cheshire Hounds in Unionville. Mention Unionville or Cheshire to a fox-hunter anywhere in the world, and a glow of recognition and appreciation instantly lights up their eyes.

While Turner rode show horses – that mecca of the show world, the Devon Horse Show, is not far from Unionville – he followed the natural progression from fox hunting into steeplechasing, and he dreamed of being a champion jockey. When he weighed 105 pounds, he dreamed of being a great flat jockey, the next Eddie Arcaro or Bill Shoemaker. Then, in 18 months, he grew six inches and added weight. He then dreamed of becoming a champion jockey in the world of steeplechasing, a small but popular branch of Thoroughbred racing in which horses must jump a series of obstacles while racing at or near full speed. It is an exciting sport and, for someone who grew up in Turner's world, just as enticing as the race track for those who gravitate to flat racing.

In pursuit of his dream, Turner ended up in a steeplechasing academy that, in the scholarly world, would be the equivalent of the Sorbonne or Oxford University. He began riding for W. Burling Cocks, a leading steeplechase rider of the 1930s who became a preeminent trainer of the last half of the 20th century and was inducted into Thoroughbred racing's Hall of Fame in 1985.

A demanding and thoroughly knowledgeable horseman, Cocks taught other horsemen as much as he trained horses. Through Cocks's Hermitage Farm stable, located between Kennett Square and Unionville, passed Hall of Fame brothers A. P. "Paddy" Smithwick and D. Michael "Mikey" Smithwick before Turner showed up, and Hall of Fame trainer Jonathan Sheppard sojourned in Cocks's establishment during Turner's final days at Hermitage. After Turner came Tom Skiffington, a champion rider and now a leading New York trainer.

For a while, from 1958 through 1962, Turner lived his dream of becoming a top steeplechase jockey. At 6-foot-2, though, his weight climbed toward the upper limits for a steeplechase rider. Although weight assignments in steeplechase racing are relatively high – a minimum of about 130 pounds as opposed to the flat-racing bottom in the 105-pound range – they still necessitate, in the slang of British jump racing, "wasting," or rapid weight reduction.

As young and impressionable riders will do, Turner tried some novel strategies for wasting. The older veteran jockeys told him that the way to lose weight fast was to be buried in a manure pile and let its natural heat pull off the excess pounds. They cooperated by burying Turner in the pile and, just for effect, put a cardboard box over his head.

Late that afternoon, "Burley" Cocks came out of the house and went over to the manure pile to investigate why an overturned card-board box was sitting atop it. Underneath the box was Turner, who was very close to passing out and thoroughly dehydrated. He revived after several quarts of water. "The old boys had told me that was how you had to do things, and being a young blood, I had to think that was the way to do things. The old boys loved it."

That is a funny (and true) story, to be sure, but another part of Turner's wasting strategy was not funny at all. While still in his teens and trying to make weight for his steeplechase mounts, he started drinking. "I got dependent on it when I was reducing to ride jumpers because it made you sweat so much easier," Turner said. He indeed may have sweated more, as the body reacts to a foreign substance, but the empty calories certainly added to the reducing effort in the long run.

Drinking was not just for losing weight; it was, Turner said, a part of the life-style. In the days when he was riding steeplechase horses, Turner crossed that line from being an alcohol abuser – someone who drinks too much – to being an alcoholic, the victim of a disease that does not allow the person to have voluntary control over the drinking.

"It was just a way of life, and so it was a perfectly natural thing to drink a lot, but you worked hard. And, as long as you were on time to work, and worked hard, and did whatever you had to do, it was an accepted part of life. It was a perfectly natural thing to do," he said.

The alcoholic also encounters another milestone, when he or she passes out of the land where alcohol is a pleasant diversion, which it is for nine out of ten people who consume alcoholic beverages, and walks into a strange world where drinking is a way of life. "There is a point at which you reach a crossroads, and the friends you seek are in a drinking situation. You tend to associate with the other people less and less. The next thing you know, you're only associating with drinking people. I was that way back when I was riding jumpers," Turner said.

In all, Turner was with Cocks for eight years. After he lost the battle of the scale and was knocked out of the saddle, Turner remained at Hermitage as Cocks's assistant trainer, and he learned the skills that would make him, in the 1970s, one of flat racing's best-respected

young horsemen. When he feels they are ready, Cocks kicks his pro-
teges out of the nest, while usually pointing them toward a patron
who will nurture a young trainer's career. Turner's patron was the
Hickory Tree Stable of James Mills.

On his own in 1966, Turner had the Hickory Tree horses in
Maryland in the spring of 1967, and went to Delaware Park for the
early summer months before shipping to Saratoga Race Course for its
August stand. After Saratoga, he shipped into Belmont Park and the
rich, competitive world of New York racing.

Like others who emerged from the steeplechase world, Turner
quickly developed a reputation for thoroughness and for a well-
rounded knowledge of the competitive horse. He came to the attention of Dr. Hill and Taylor, partners who wanted a significant role in
how their horse was managed. Their philosophy was grounded on
well-established ownership principles that, at that time, were rarely
followed in the horse business. Then, and sometimes now, the trainer was not unlike the autocratic orchestra conductor who chose the
repertoire, directed all of the notes, and, from the owner, demanded
loyalty and a steady flow of cash.

Hill and Taylor were attracted to Turner's talents, and in the summer of 1975, they sent him a jewel among jewels, Seattle Slew. On
pedigree, the Bold Reasoning colt out of My Charmer, by Poker,
probably was worth his purchase price. Bred and raised by Ben S.
Castleman only a short distance from the Lexington sales pavilion
where he was sold for $17,500, Slew was shipped to Maryland, where
Turner broke him to the saddle in the fall of 1975.

For a time, he was just another racing prospect, and it was only in
the spring of 1976, shortly before he joined Turner in New York, that
Slew began to separate himself from the breed. "He had never breezed
or anything," Turner said. "But he showed that he was a very, very
independent thinker. And you combine that with the physique that
goes with a runner, then you had the mental thing to go with the
physique. Then all you had to do was let him mature, and you had a
race horse."

But Slew had something that made him a king among commoners,
and it was an unexpected characteristic that transcended the raw talent. "He had insanity, a burning desire to run," Turner said. "He did-

n't know what 'stop' was; never figured it out. That set him apart from the rest of them. I have never been around one who was so extreme, either before or since. The mental thing set him apart from all the rest that I've been around."

Slew's insanity carried him through three races without a defeat in 1976, including a victory in the Champagne Stakes, in which he pulled away in the stretch to a 9 3/4-length victory over For the Moment. That convincing victory, combined with his fast time for the Champagne's mile (1:34 2/5) earned Seattle Slew his first Eclipse Award, as the champion two-year-old colt. He had never been tested, and after he won Hialeah Park's Flamingo Stakes in 1977 (by four lengths over Giboulee), he was attracting the attention of every turf writer in America.

One of the best, and best-known, was Billy Reed, a product of Kentucky who, after a time at Sports Illustrated, had become the sports editor of the Louisville *Courier-Journal*. It would be Reed's job at the *Courier-Journal* to write the main story chronicling the 1977 Kentucky Derby in the hometown of the Run for the Roses. Reed continued his year-long preparations by traveling to New York before the Wood Memorial Stakes at Aqueduct Race Track to interview Turner, the 37-year-old phenomenon who trained the best horse to come along since Secretariat.

When Reed asked where he could find Turner, he was directed to a bar across Plainfield Avenue from Belmont Park's stable gate. There, in the company of other drinkers, Turner held court. A friendly but fundamentally shy person, Turner developed many friends and allies among the turf writers. They chronicled his triumphs, and some of the writers drank with him. Uncomfortable with the issue, some of them virtually ignored the growing discontent of the owners with Turner's drinking.

Coached by Frank Tours, then an official of the New York Racing Association, which operates Aqueduct, Belmont, and Saratoga, Turner handled the media crush with amazing aplomb. "Dealing with all the people involved was difficult. That horse had more media coverage than Secretariat, who was the phenomenon of the past 30 years, and it was because he was the undefeated horse. And it kept going on," Turner said. "He was unique in that he was going for the Triple

Crown undefeated, and no horse had ever done that. There's a mystique that goes with undefeated horses, and that sets them apart from all the rest. The public loves that."

Was Turner drinking at the time? No question. Was he an active alcoholic? By his own admission, most certainly. Asked that latter question, Turner provided an anecdotal answer. "My bar bill at Churchill Downs was $14,000. I had all the press there, and none of them were drinking tea," he said.

Slew won the Derby by 1 3/4 lengths over Run Dusty Run, and his natural speed gave him the second jewel of the Triple Crown, the Preakness at Baltimore, by 1 1/2 lengths over Iron Constitution. With each victory – the Preakness was his eighth without a defeat – the pressure ratcheted up a notch or two. "The gamblers, the experienced old boys, started betting against him because, well, he's got to lose. Those things have to happen," Turner said. "Andy Beyer (the Washington *Post* columnist and author of several popular handicapping books) was a classic example of that. He bet against him in every one of the Triple Crown races because the biggest reason was that he didn't think that he could win another one."

Well, he did win that next one, the Belmont Stakes, and became the tenth Triple Crown winner. Turner, however, did not see that ultimate victory, the pinnacle of any horse trainer. He was busy trying to get a drink in Belmont's clubhouse, which was jammed as a result of Seattle Slew's unique celebrity.

Billy Reed, an outstanding reporter who knows the value of eyewitness testimony, was following Turner's every step, and they stopped at a bar so that Turner could get a vodka and grapefruit juice. For Turner, the job was completed; he had saddled Slew and put jockey Jean Cruguet into the saddle. "The only thing that could cost that horse a race was the unexpected, the unforeseen. I felt I had done my job," he said.

The Belmont bartender, either overwhelmed by the crowd or oblivious to Turner's celebrity, refused to let him cut into the line for his drink and sent him to the back of the crowd. While Turner was negotiating his drink, Reed was watching the race on a television monitor and giving the trainer a pole-by-pole account. Finally, Slew accomplished the seemingly impossible, carrying his speed over the

Belmont's 1 1/2 miles and winning by four lengths over Run Dusty Run. "I was the first reporter ever to tell a trainer that his horse had just won the Triple Crown," Reed wrote in 1989 – more than two years before Turner's brush with death.

That moment, which Turner all but missed while getting a drink, was the high point of the Slew and Billy story. Turner knew that the Triple Crown had taken its toll on Seattle Slew, and he wanted to stop on him for a time, to allow the wear and tear of the long campaign to heal and tighten. The owners, determined to manage their asset, disagreed, and insisted that Seattle Slew run in the $300,000 Swaps Stakes – named for the California invader who had defeated Nashua in the 1955 Kentucky Derby – at Hollywood Park on July 3. So, three weeks after the Belmont, Slew was shipped across the continent to run in a major stakes race.

Hill and Taylor "thought, shucks, there won't be anything in the race out there. It will be a cakewalk," Turner said. But Slew sustained the first defeat of his ten-race career against a field that would not have been competitive against him if he had been at the top of his game. Slew finished fourth, beaten 16 lengths by winner J. O. Tobin. "Well, you can only go to the well so many times, then you have to recharge the battery. And the battery was run down after the Belmont," Turner said. "You get battle fatigue. Battle fatigue is when you've been under pressure for so long and your adrenal system gives up. They need to be recharged, and it's the same thing with horses."

Five years later, when the Taylors and Hills were racing Slew o' Gold, a top son of Seattle Slew, Mickey Taylor told members of the turf media that he and Hill had been mistaken in running Slew in the Swaps, that they had underestimated how much the Triple Crown campaign had taken out of him. Seattle Slew did not race again in 1977, but he nonetheless was voted Horse of the Year as well as three-year-old male champion. Turner was voted 1977's leading trainer by the New York Turf Writers Association.

But before the awards were handed out, a further humiliation awaited Turner in Seattle, where the colt was paraded at Longacres Race Track – against the trainer's wishes – shortly after the Hollywood Park defeat. "Morris Alhadeff, who owned Longacres then, sprung one on me. He called me out before 30,000 people and said: 'Now, I want you to tell these people what happened that our horse lost in the Swaps Stakes.' That is putting you on the spot, knowing that I didn't want to be there in the first place," Turner said. "I just reached back and, off the top of my head – I don't know where it came from – I said: 'Mr. Alhadeff, this is one place where we carried the impossible dream one step too far.' I got it off, but I don't know where that came from, other than that I always was a fan of Don Quixote."

Within a few months, Billy Turner's impossible dream had ended. Seattle Slew and the other horses were taken from Turner – without notice, although the owners had been becoming increasingly vocal about their concerns over their trainer's drinking – and given to Doug Peterson. Turner had a big reputation, bountiful media-generated sympathy, a lot of empty stalls, and a growing alcoholism problem. His next major client was Richard Winn, a Philadelphia-area businessman who owned Welcome Farm in Pottstown, about 20 miles directly north of the Unionville area where Turner had grown up.

Winn, an amiable developer and racing fan, put together a crack team to find top racing prospects at the yearling sales in the early 1980s. Turner was the trainer and adviser on athletic qualities, William G. Munn consulted on the pedigrees, and Dr. Jack McGuire looked at the yearlings and offered judgments on their fitness for racing. The team would have considerable success for a while, but Winn became concerned about his trainer. In 1982, he convinced Turner to enter an alcoholism treatment center. Turner came out of rehab and again was at the top of the game.

"The best year I ever had training race horses, if you throw out the few stars, was in 1983," said Turner, who had Winn's best horse, Bay Shore Stakes (G2) winner Strike Gold that spring, and Welcome Farm's turf specialist Kilauea winner of the Lexington Handicap that year. "That lasted through 1984, when I had Play On (winner of the Withers Stakes and second to Gate Dancer in the 1984 Preakness), and I had a very good year for Dogwood in 1985. But then the drinking started to creep up on me again, because I wasn't convinced I had a problem. And then it was a steady progression down to 1991, when I was almost out of here."

He was almost gone because, when he thought he was handling the drinking, the drinking was handling him. "The end for me was, you really don't want to have anything to do with it any more, and there is no way in the world that you can live without it. You're stuck," he said. Turner remembers nothing of that week before July 5, 1991, but his intention was crystal clear. He quit eating and drank steadily, undoubtedly intent on drinking himself to death. "It had beaten me. I was finished," he said.

It was then that Barbara Turner called two friends from his Hermitage Farm days, Louis "Paddy" Neilson III and Douglas Small Jr. Turner was so weak that they literally carried him to Small's car. "Dougie and Paddy Neilson came up, and they were going to take me down and put me in Ashley. Going down the road, they thought I had died," Turner said. "Dougie had a phone in his car, and he called ahead and said, 'Well, you better have an ambulance down there.' They shot me off to the hospital." He spent ten days in a hospital in Bel Air, Maryland. "They had a trickle (of intravenous fluids) on me for four straight days, 24 hours a day," Turner said. "Then I felt fine. I was ready to go. You become older and wiser in a hurry, though."

Turner spent five weeks in Father Martin's Ashley, an institution in Havre de Grace that is heavily supported by Maryland's horse people and many others. Among the lessons that Turner acquired in becoming older and wiser quickly was that the damage of decades of alcoholism is not corrected overnight – if ever. "I know I didn't get my balance back for a good two years. My short-term memory is still coming back," he said in mid-1994.

For Billy Turner, life is better. He is more peaceful and, as advocated by 12-step programs, lives one day at a time; he remains sober one day at a time as he continues his recovery from a disease that has no cure. He is now based at Maryland's Laurel Race Course with a stable of about 20 horses. "I am enjoying training race horses again. I really didn't like it anymore for a while. I had lost interest in everything. The desire to succeed had gone. Once that's gone, you can't do anything. You're just going through the motions," he said.

He also learned emphatically that just wanting to quit drinking is not enough. Turner and other alcoholics want to quit drinking, but the disease refuses to loosen its grip on them. "You can't do it yourself. That's what we all learn if we are lucky enough to live that long. That's what it took for me to learn," Turner said. "I was just a little bit luckier than some others. Just a little bit luckier. Not much."

DOUG'S STORY

Douglas R. Peterson was a child prodigy, a boy wonder. He left home for the race track at age 14 and four years later became the youngest person ever to saddle the winner of a race worth more than $100,000. By the time he was 26, he was training one of the greatest horses of all time, Seattle Slew.

Life was, from all appearances, very good. Well before his 30th birthday, he owned assets approaching $3-million. He had it all: a barnful of good horses as well as a champion; two houses and a condo; and a Cadillac in each of the driveways.

As fast as Doug Peterson's wealth piled up, it went away just as quickly – or even faster. He was a child prodigy on the race track, but he was also a precocious drinker. Almost as soon as he went to the race track full-time, he could put away a case of beer between noon and feeding time.

Doug Peterson lost everything to his disease, followed his alcohol addiction into cocaine addiction, and botched a suicide attempt because he fell on his hemorrhaging wrist and cut off the flow of blood. He was on the streets, almost without possessions and totally stripped of self-respect. "That was the biggest loss of all," he said.

Almost by chance, he found his way to the Winners Foundation trailer at California's Santa Anita Park in January 1987. In what he describes as an instant of clarity, Doug Peterson reached out, asked for help, and chose life. Today, Peterson has a solid stable of about 17 runners on the Southern California circuit. He lives one day at a time and, through a 12-step program, has found spiritual meaning in his life. He also has taken that final step of the recovering alcoholic; he is helping others to find help for their fatal disease. Yes, Doug Peterson is a winner.

Peterson grew up in Littleton, Colorado, not far from Centennial Park. Although his family was not associated with racing, young Doug was irresistibly attracted to the strange world behind the track's fences. "At the age of 11, I'd ride my bicycle past the track and look in the chain-link fence," he said. "I guess one day I looked too hard, and I went inside and got a job.

"And I went to work for this man," Peterson said at the 1993 Conference on Alcohol and Drug Abuse Programs for the Horse Racing Industry. "He said, 'There's two things that are not going to happen.' And he said, 'The first thing is, you're not going to get paid.' I shrugged my shoulders and said, 'Okay.' He said, 'The second thing is you won't touch a horse.' That was pretty hard, but I said, 'Okay.'

"So I carried water, raked, carried hay, did all these things for about two weeks. I would get there about 4 in the morning and stay all day, stay till it was dark. And after two weeks, he said: 'You know, I think I'm going to pay you.' The guy gave me $25 a week, and that's how I got started at the track. I worked for this man during the summer, and continued to do that on a part-time basis."

Peterson became a racetracker, for life. "The horses and the track, they get into your blood, then you're hooked. I left home when I was 14, and I've been at the track ever since," he said. His parents insisted only that he obtain a high-school education, and he received his diploma in New Mexico. "I worked very hard, went to school. My grades were just enough to make it, but that wasn't important to me. It was the horses and the track that were important to me."

Shortly after he went to the race track, Peterson began his love affair with beer. "I liked beer. I would drink warm beer, and it didn't take me long when I was 14, only a few weeks that I got to where I could drink a warm case of beer in between lunchtime and the time to go back, and not anybody would know about it. I had a very high tolerance, and I continued to drink more and more," he said. "I think I was an alcoholic from the start. After I got the taste of beer and could hold that much, I was an alcoholic."

His drinking, however, was not unusual or aberrant behavior on the track. Far from it. "There's a lot of drinking around the track. Most of the backside help drink, and that's one of the main activities. There aren't a lot of things to do back there. I think it's very easy to get into that," he said.

By 18, he had obtained his trainer's license and saddled the two-year-old filly Texas Sky to defeat colts in the Land of Enchantment Futurity at New Mexico's La Mesa Park in 1970, thus becoming the youngest person ever to train the winner of a $100,000-plus race. Before too long, he was headed east, toward New York. "Any number of people told me: 'Doug, if you really want to amount to something or to go somewhere with this thing, you have to go to New York, you have to get to the Big Apple," he said.

"There wasn't year-round racing the way there is now. You bounced from town to town. So I made my way on to Chicago, from Chicago to Florida, and then started working my way to New York. I went to New York in 1971," he said. "It was a good move for me, and another stepping stone."

While Seattle Slew dazzled the racing world in 1977, Peterson was an assistant trainer for Bob Dunham in New York and had two horses that he trained himself. Toward the end of the year, Dr. Jim Hill and Mickey Taylor came to see him.

"They came to me one week on a Thursday, and they said: "Doug, we want to meet with you for lunch.' I met with them for lunch, and they said: 'You can't tell anybody this, but we want to make a change. You were going to be our second trainer, and now we're going to give you all of the horses. But first we want you to think about this and make sure that you want to train Seattle Slew and that you want all of the pressure, the whole stable, and everything that goes with it. We want you to take a week, then meet us next Thursday for lunch and tell us.' I knew what I wanted as soon as they asked me," Peterson said.

"Hell yes, I wanted to do it. So I waited and never said a word. What they said was: 'You're going to get on a plane and fly to Florida, and in the middle of the night we're going to move the horses down to Florida, so Billy won't know a thing, and they did that. The next thing I knew, they were in Florida, and I had a private job with 32 head of horses."

From the beginning, the job was no picnic for Peterson. A virulent strain of colitis hit the stable early in 1978, and the horse stabled next to Seattle Slew died. Slew contracted the disorder and almost died, too. While Slew recovered, and while his ability to come back from the illness was still a question, Hill and Taylor sold half of the Horse of the Year for $6-million. Thus, Seattle Slew had a value of $12-million, far more than the syndication of Secretariat – albeit before his Triple Crown campaign – only five years earlier. Doug Peterson was now training, in dollar terms, the most valuable horse ever to set foot on a race track.

He put Slew back together again, and the colt won his first start of 1978 on Mother's Day at Aqueduct. Racing over a sloppy track, Slew won the seven-furlong allowance by 8 1/4 lengths in 1:22 4/5. A few days after that victory, the stable announced that Slew had sustained a hock injury in his stall and would not run in the Metropolitan Handicap on Memorial Day.

In fact, Slew would not race again until August 12, when the owners pressured NYRA Chairman Ogden Mills "Dinny" Phipps to have the racing office write an allowance race for Seattle Slew. The track again came up sloppy, but Slew sloshed to an easy victory in 1:21 3/5, three-fifths off the Saratoga record. When the Slew Crew could not find another race for him in New York, Peterson had to send him into the Meadowlands Race Track's Paterson Handicap, which was run on Labor Day evening under the lights.

Slew had never raced under the lights, and he had one other thing going against him in the Paterson: Angel Cordero Jr. A Hall of Fame jockey and a masterful rider, Cordero was to ride Tartan Farms' Dr. Patches, and he turned his psychological-warfare skills on Cruguet, who had continued as Seattle Slew's rider through the trainer change.

"Cordero is great at intimidating people. That night when they got to the jocks room, wherever Cruguet went, Cordero went. He was in his ear that he was going to beat him all night long. He psyched him out before the race," Peterson said. Slew opened his usual early lead, but he tired in the stretch and was caught by Dr. Patches, who won by a neck after a long battle through the lane.

After that, Cruguet was off Seattle Slew, and Cordero was on him. "I went into the jocks room and fired Cruguet and hired Cordero. That was quite an experience, having to do that," Peterson said. For a while, the change appeared to be – and was – a stroke of genius. Seattle Slew went into the $300,000 Marlboro Cup at Belmont on September 16 and proved that he was everything he had been at three, and probably more.

In the field of six for the 1 1/8-mile Marlboro was Affirmed, winner of the 1978 Triple Crown and the race's 1-2 favorite after Slew's Meadowlands defeat. Never before had two Triple Crown winners met on the race track, and Seattle Slew's owners were unsure how he would stack up against the three-year-old. "I was told the night before: 'If this horse couldn't win, don't run him.' If I had any doubt in my mind, because it would ruin him as a stallion," Peterson said.

But the young trainer was sure, and Seattle Slew fulfilled his expectations – and then some. Slew jumped out to a quick two-length lead, and Cordero put everyone to sleep, walking through a quarter mile in :24 and the half-mile in :47.

With Affirmed in pursuit, Slew cruised through the next quarter mile in :23 1/5, getting the first six furlongs in 1:10 1/5, before accelerating to the furlong pole and completing the mile in a very swift 1:33 3/5. Steve Cauthen had Affirmed under a drive, but to no effect. Slew crossed the wire with three lengths on the other Triple Crown winner and completed the nine furlongs in 1:45 4/5, only two-fifths of a second off Secretariat's world record.

Affirmed passed up the $163,000 Woodward Stakes two weeks later to await the Jockey Club Gold Cup. Slew's only serious competition in the 1 1/4-mile Woodward was Exceller, but Cordero again jumped out of the gate quickly and slowed the pace virtually to a walk, completing the first half mile in :47 3/5. The game was over, and Slew won by four lengths in two minutes flat.

The 1 1/2-mile Jockey Club Gold Cup came up in another two weeks, on October 14, and the track was sloppy for the renewal of the two Triple Crown winners' rivalry. On the clubhouse turn of the huge race track, though, Affirmed's saddle slipped and Cauthen found himself with little control and pressing the early pace of Seattle Slew. They rolled through suicidal fractions – :22 3/5 for the quarter, :45 1/5 for the half, and 1:09 2/5 for six furlongs – before Affirmed packed it in after seven furlongs.

Cordero gave Slew a bit of a breather, reaching the start of the final turn after a mile in 1:35 2/5. Slew appeared to be in control, until Exceller and jockey Bill Shoemaker appeared out of nowhere. Charging from approximately 10 lengths off the pace, Exceller hurtled along the inside rail and drew nearly abreast of Seattle Slew at the quarter pole, just as the leaders reached the homestretch.

"Cordero has him out in the middle of the race track, and he never saw or heard Shoemaker coming. He went by him on the inside of him, and startled him like a bug boy," Peterson said. "He said, 'Doug,

I went from a hold to a drive in one jump.' Then he started gathering him and setting him down."

Slew had lost the tactical advantage but not his insane desire to run. He fought every inch of the way to the wire, and Cordero used his superior strength to draw every last ounce of effort out of his mount. But, at the wire, Exceller won by a nose.

"Cordero apologized. He said he got the horse beat. Seattle Slew's greatest race came in defeat, unfortunately," Peterson said. "This horse laid the body down going a mile and a half in the mud, with the first three-quarters in nine and change. In the mud at Belmont Park, going a mile and a half, that was just unheard of for a horse to do that."

Seattle Slew completed his career in his next start, the $100,000 Stuyvesant Handicap at Aqueduct on November 10. The idea was to send him to stud on a winning note, and he won by 3 1/4 lengths over mediocre competition. Doug Peterson, the young man thrust into the spotlight with one of racing's great horses, had not dropped the ball. If anything, he had added to the asset's value and burnished the reputation of a genuine superstar.

That was not to say, however, that he was not having problems with his drinking. His only advantage, albeit a fleeting one, was his youth. "The younger you are, the better you can function and get away with a lot of that stuff," he said. "As you get a little older, you can't hide it as well, and you can't function as well. Your body doesn't respond as well, and mentally, you're not nearly as sharp. It's a double duty. I had youth going for me then. I was only 26. I think that was a big help to me in handling everything, the pressure and everything else. Hell, you don't think about it. But obviously the progression of the disease was getting to me."

After Slew retired, Peterson took the Taylor-Hill stable to California for the winter of 1979. "I brought them to Santa Anita, and I had a very good meet; things went well. But my drinking, the disease, was escalating now," he said. The private job ended in 1980, as the partnership cut back on its racing stable to await Slew's first crop of runners. "By the end of 1980, the handwriting was pretty much on the wall," he said.

Now operating as a public trainer, Peterson tried to maintain stables in both New York and Maryland, and he was not handling it well. "I'm trying to fly back between Maryland and New York, and that's all I needed, for an alcoholic to sit in an airport or in an airplane and get drunk. That's very handy," he said.

Finally, in late 1980, Doug Peterson fled the wreckage of his career and his life. "I was in New York, and I was about to lose my home, although I didn't know it at the time. I was about to lose it, and I think I was drunk two days before Christmas, and I just took off to California," he said.

"I'm out here with no horses and no clients, I'm b.s.-ing my way with the press, and just living in a fantasy world. I was becoming more dysfunctional as time went on. I ended up just going around the track doing nothing. It got to the point where I wouldn't go out to the track in the morning, but would go out in the afternoons and watch the races and get drunk."

For the former millionaire, it was a long and pain-filled descent to bottom. He used marijuana and cocaine, spent some time in the Arcadia, California, jail, and became as mean as a junkyard dog. "I was a very angry and violent man. At that point, I was just sitting and waiting in the bar to get into a fight every night. It had gotten into a very violent situation," he said. "At that point, the Arcadia police had had so much and were so fed up that they were just going to lock me away and have me committed to a mental institution."

Alcoholism had stripped his life of all dignity and all meaning, and Peterson tried to end the pain. But, for some reason, he survived. "Fortunately, in a suicide attempt, I had slashed my wrist, and my wrist went underneath me and cut off the flow of blood. I was picked up, and brought into the emergency room," Peterson said. "A friend of mine had come into the emergency room, and he said that if they didn't take me to the nut house he would take me to a psychiatrist every day. He was going to pay for it. That's the only reason I was saved from that at that time."

Visits with the psychiatrist avoided the institutionalization, but Peterson had little trouble hiding the root problem. "I had a disease called alcoholism. Everybody wanted to dance around it. Nobody wanted to confront it," he said. Doug Peterson finally hit bottom in January of 1987, when he took a woman with whom he was living to the Winners Foundation trailer at Santa Anita Park, which is located in Arcadia, a Los Angeles suburb. He was going to solve his problems by getting her some help.

"I took her to the Winners Foundation for her drinking and crying all day long and all night," he said. He warned the Winners Foundation case worker that, if he came back and found that the woman was crying, he intended to dismantle the foundation's trailer. "I was going to remodel that thing, because I told that guy there: 'Don't you make her cry, whatever you do.' Sure enough, she was crying when I got back, and he tried to talk to me through the window," Peterson said.

"It was a thing. He was trying to get her to speak to me: 'Please don't go any further with this. If you really want to get back together with her, if you really want this thing to work, she wants you to come back tomorrow. I really thought, as sick as I was, that it would be different tomorrow and that I could go back there and I was going for her.

"Somehow – it's strange how people get it – but in going back I had that moment of clarity. That's where the turning point was," Peterson said. "Sick as I was, I wanted anything, any kind of help."

With the foundation's help, he admitted himself to a halfway house, the Bishop Gooden Home, which was supported by Louis R. Rowan, the California real-estate executive, avid racing fan, Thoroughbred breeder, and alcoholic who founded the Winners Foundation. Anonymous donations allowed Peterson to remain in the halfway house for six months. Ironically, the young woman whom Peterson took to the Winners Foundation never did get help.

Once the trainer of one of the world's greatest horses, Peterson started his road back by working in the racing office at Los Alamitos, the race track of the Orange County Fair in Southern California. "I was an entry clerk in the morning. It took a lot of humility, taking entries from trainers, people who I thought couldn't even spell 'h-o-r-s-e' and here they are training horses, and I'm working as a flunky in the office," Peterson said. "I worked on the starting gate at night, and that required more humility. I started out as the flag man the first night, but somebody got hurt in the first race, and they let me handle the horses. I did that the entire meet. Then I was given some horses to train, one at a time."

One horse led to another, and "it continually gets better, the quality of horses, the quality of my clientele," he said. "Everything gets better. There have been a lot of slow, little steps. But those are the good, solid ones for me. Those quick fixes always got me in trouble, never lasted; and today life is good, and I'm learning how to live."

Peterson has explored the spiritual side of recovery, and that has led him to a new, fulfilling stage of his life. "And hopefully I find help for other people. I sponsor people on and off at the track. I want to make myself available," he said. Doug Peterson again is a winner, both on and off the track.

Chapter 2

Enemies of the People

Without question, alcohol and drugs – both their abuse and addictions to them – are scourges that rip at the fabric of society in the United States, Canada, and many other industrialized countries. Their costs, both in lives and dollars, are enormous. Abraham J. Twerski, M.D., one of the country's recognized authorities in the field, described substance abuse as "the most serious public health problem of this generation." [1]

If these scourges afflict society generally, no one should be surprised that they are also causing problems in the horse racing industries and all horse-related enterprises. The circumstances and problems that exist outside the fences – in society generally – inevitably make their way inside the fences of our continent's racing enclosures. If these maladies can seize such well-known individuals as Billy Turner and Doug Peterson and take them to the very edge of the chasm, they can certainly affect others within the industry, whether they are trainers, grooms, caretakers, hotwalkers, veterinarians, farriers, drivers, jockeys, mutuel clerks, concessionaire employees – or even the president of the race track.

No reliable data are available, but it has been estimated by counselors on the front lines that 30 to 40 percent of North America's backstretch workers abuse alcohol, and that is more than a problem. It is an epidemic. As abuse of both alcohol and drugs and addictions to them are explored in the remainder of this chapter, it will be noted that the estimate for backstretch alcoholism is three to four times the rate of alcohol addiction found in the U.S. population generally. In addition to laying out some of the facts about alcohol and drug addiction, this chapter also will explore the costs of these addictions to society. And, the chapter will look at a further problem – found both inside and outside the fences – over how society regards addictions and the scientifically recognized fact that they are progressive, fatal diseases.

Let us repeat the most important word in that statement – diseases. Alcohol and drug addictions are not under voluntary control; the people who have them rarely can do anything about them without some help from outside themselves. Many times we think that we can pit willpower against them, but that's really quite foolish. That is like pitting willpower against cancer or a broken leg.

The Rev. John Mayton, speaking at the first Conference on Alcohol and Drug Abuse Programs for the Horse Racing Industry at Louisville, Kentucky, in 1989, starkly laid out how addictions imprison their victims and place them under a death sentence. "I am an alcoholic and an addict, and I invested a lot of time and money in that. And it was a lot of fun for a long time. I really enjoyed myself while I did that, because it felt a lot better to do drugs and alcohol than it did to live without them. And then after a while, the chemicals that I was abusing affected my body and my mind to a degree where I didn't enjoy that anymore. There was nothing to enjoy. And so I tried to commit suicide, and I was serious about it. And thankfully I was unsuccessful," said Mayton, who subsequently was sent by his parole officer to a substance-abuse treatment center. Mayton, who served as a chaplain at race tracks in Washington and was director of the Winners Foundation in California, subsequently helped to administer the Ryan Family Foundation grants totaling more than $1-million to set up substance-abuse treatment programs on 54 North American race tracks in 1989 and 1990.

Here is another voice of recovery, from the 1993 Louisville Conference: "I tried to be responsible, but the alcohol controlled me to the point – the alcohol became my god, and it ran my life. It told me, it dictated to me. It told me what to do, and how to do it, and whenever."

Robert Frierson, M.D., a University of Louisville Medical School professor and medical director of the Jefferson Alcohol and Drug Abuse Center in Louisville, noted at the first Louisville Conference in 1989 that some drugs were initially regarded as "safe," meaning that they could be abused without a strong likelihood of addiction.

"We believed for a long time that cocaine was not physically addicting, that it was just a recreational drug, that there was no physical dependence associated with that drug. We were certainly wrong about that. We believed for a long time that marijuana was only psychologically addicting and not physically addicting – we were certainly wrong about that. So at this point, the distinction between drugs that are psychologically and physically addicting is very narrow. And we realize now that a person can become addicted to just about anything, and we certainly see that. People who are detoxified from one drug are very susceptible to misusing any drug they might be taking," he said.

"Basically, psychological addiction involves such things as craving and drug-seeking behavior. And this usually involves things like forging prescriptions, or going out and obtaining the drugs illegally. And, for many people, this sense of adventure is a major part of the attraction of drug use. But the psychological addiction is much harder to deal with than the physical addiction." Physical addiction is, in the broadest terms, characterized by a tolerance to the addictive substance – requiring larger and larger doses to achieve the desired effect – and withdrawal. With alcohol and other depressants, the withdrawal may include seizures.

Dr. Frierson said the addiction does not require every day use of the substance. "I have people who come to me and say: 'Well, I only smoke pot once a week, so I don't have a problem.' Of course, we know now about marijuana, that it can stay in the bloodstream for two, three, four weeks, even. So somebody who smokes pot once a week always has some cannabis in their bloodstream. That's the first thing.

"The second thing is that it's more a measure of what you do when you're using the drug and how much control you have over stopping the using. So if I have someone who tells me: 'I smoke pot once a year, but when I smoke I beat up my wife and tear up the furniture, and I do this and I do that, but I don't think I have a problem' – you do," he said.

Another characteristic of addiction is that it produces antisocial behavior. It produces a constant danger and a risk in the workplace, and there's no doubt that it requires treatment or some treatment equivalent. The most famous treatment equivalent is Alcoholics Anonymous; other 12-step programs, such as Narcotics Anonymous or Cocaine Anonymous, have developed on the model of AA.

ALCOHOL

Other than the nicotine found in cigarettes, alcohol is the most commonly used drug in America. Approximately 68 percent of American adults consume at least one alcoholic drink a year [2], and most people use alcohol socially and safely. Why do we use alcohol? We use alcohol for a very good reason: To have a temporary euphoria and, in many cases, to achieve relaxation. We drink socially to celebrate a happy event, a promotion at work, or a victory on the race track.

In terms of its seriousness, the next step beyond social use of alcohol is abuse. Most people who get in trouble with alcohol are abusers: their occasional overdose lands them in jail for driving under the influence or in a similar problem. Naive people misusing a substance that they do not understand very well are more likely to get into trouble than other people.

Alcoholism needs to be differentiated from alcohol abuse, because an alcohol problem cannot be equated with the disease. While alcoholics have a compulsion to drink, the alcohol abuser often can change his or her drinking habits to reduce the risk of social or legal difficulties. [3]

Among users of alcohol, about one in ten ever develops the disease of alcoholism. Rates of alcoholism are about 10 percent of the U.S. population for men and 5 percent for women, although the numbers have been converging in recent years. [4] The number of Americans suffering from alcoholism is estimated at between 9 million and 10 million. [5]

Alcoholism is a killer; an alcoholic will live ten to 12 fewer years than someone who is not suffering from the disease. [6] It causes 95,000 deaths per year, and even that large number may be underestimated because hospitals and other institutions do not necessarily look for alcoholism as the primary factor in a death. In a review of the officially listed cause of death for 1,823 diagnosed, practicing alcoholics, alcoholism was listed as the cause of death in only 9 percent of the cases.

In 1986, chronic liver disease and cirrhosis, the principal chronic diseases associated with alcoholism, was the nation's ninth leading killer, claiming 26,000 lives. [7] Alcohol also is regarded as a cause of many accidental deaths, including auto crashes, falls, fires, and burns. In

1987, half of the nation's auto fatalities involved alcohol.[8] The risk of a fatal crash, per mile driven, is at least eight times higher for a drunk driver than for a sober one. [9] Louisville's Norton Psychiatric Clinic has found that many near-fatal falls among the elderly are related to alcohol.

Alcoholics commit suicide at six to 15 times the rate of the general population. Approximately 20 to 36 percent of suicide victims have histories of alcohol abuse or were drinking shortly before their suicides. In addition, alcohol was more often associated with suicides that were impulsive rather than premeditated. [10]

Alcoholism is a serious problem for the nation's 10 million alcoholics, and it also a family disease. Alcoholism often shatters marriages and disrupts family life. There also is growing evidence that it is passed from one generation to the next. Studies of adopted children in the 1970s found that there was a high incidence of alcoholism in the sons when the biological fathers were alcoholics. Similarly, there was a much lower correlation between alcoholism in the sons and alcoholism in their stepfathers. [11] In short, the data suggest a genetic link for the disease. Fetal alcohol syndrome is a major cause of mental retardation and birth defects. With this disorder, the effects of the alcoholism are carried into the next generation, even before that next generation is born. The costs, as we will see later, are staggering.

Who are the alcoholics? It is an equal-opportunity disease, without doubt, but certain patterns have been found by researchers. Of 1.4 million persons treated for alcohol abuse and dependence in fiscal year 1987, three of four were male, one-third were between the ages of 25 and 34, and one-quarter fell in the 35-to-44 age group. More than 70 percent of the admissions were white, but African Americans, Hispanics, and Native Americans were represented in greater numbers than their proportions of the total U.S. population. [12] Other studies have found that alcoholism is more prevalent in urban areas, [13] where race tracks are concentrated and from which most race tracks draw their work forces. Higher prevalence rates also are found in lower socioeconomic groups and among those with lower educational attainment. [14] A study of female alcoholics found a correlation with unemployment, relative youth, and the presence of a heavy-drinking partner. [15]

Two other facts are worth noting. Just because an alcoholic has "dried out" or become sober does not mean that he or she is out of the woods. The forest of alcoholism is very, very deep. It will take nine to 15 months for the alcohol effect to work its way out of the central nervous system. The implication of this fact is that relapse is a part of the disease and the recovery process. Because someone resumes drinking after treatment does not mean that the person is "weak." It means that the individual is still getting rid of the physical vestiges of the addiction. The support of Alcoholics Anonymous or other treatment equivalents is all the more important at those times.

Recovery from alcoholism is, in fact, a process that never ends. As one recovering alcoholic said: "When they throw the second shovelful of dirt on my casket, then they can say, 'Well, at least his alcoholism is cured.' " For the living, it will take two to five years from the last drink to develop a resilient program that will keep the recovering alcoholic sober.

Perhaps the most troubling statistic, though, was stated by Dr. Harvey R. St. Clair, associate professor at the University of Louisville School of Medicine: "Over 80 percent of the alcohol-abusing population are not getting treatment for it despite the marked increase in treatment facilities in recent years." [16] The proportion of race track personnel without a source of treatment is much, much higher.

DRUG ABUSE AND ADDICTION

America's cities, large and small, are suffering through an epidemic of illegal drugs, with drive-by shootings and muggings an unfortunate part of the urban landscape. Although alcohol is the drug of choice of most Americans and undoubtedly most members of the backstretch community of race tracks, illegal drugs are a growing concern as the work force becomes more transient and more urban. The tendency within American society is toward hiring more police officers and throwing the drug offenders in jail. They are, after all, "bad" people, in this view. But the racing industry is only one example of how some good people have gotten mixed up with some very bad stuff.

Speaking in 1989, Dr. Frierson noted that cocaine is a $40-billion a year industry in the United States alone, and it thus is a significant factor in the urban community. The number of users has climbed dramatically in a relatively short time. Twenty-five years ago, cocaine users numbered 10,000; a decade later, users had climbed to 100,000. And then the epidemic began. In 1989, Dr. Frierson estimated that between 10 million and 15 million people regularly used cocaine, and another 5 million experimented with its use.

"And this is primarily a measure of the fact that cocaine is in many forms that are more accessible now to people who are indigent," he said, and the most common is crack cocaine, which is essentially free-based cocaine that can be smoked. "With the crack cocaine – there are many people who could not afford it before but can afford it now," Dr. Frierson said. "The cost of cocaine has steadily gone down. Crack is a marketing ploy. What you've done is that you've lowered the price of cocaine to $15 to $20, and then you're able to get all new addicts who would never have been involved with the drug before. So we see cocaine being sold on grade-school and elementary-school play-grounds; we're seeing people who used to use other drugs who now can afford to use crack. And one of the things about crack is that the first use is almost always a good experience. So the addiction to crack occurs right after the first use. Very rarely do you have a bad experience the first time it's smoked."

Like alcohol, cocaine is a killer. One of the principal examples was the death of Len Bias, the star University of Maryland basketball play-er who died of a cocaine overdose while celebrating his selection by the Boston Celtics and the prospective start of his professional career. On a national level, cocaine-related deaths tripled from 1984 to 1988, Dr. Frierson said, and cocaine-related illnesses rose from 7,000 cases to more than 39,000.

Is cocaine the only drug subject to abuse and addiction? Of course not. The list is long, and it includes marijuana, heroin, Quaaludes, amphetamines, steroids, and barbiturates. Some of them are controlled substances, and others are legal medications that are obtained illegally. In many cases, they are used in combination with drugs such as cocaine or alcohol, and the result sometimes will be dual addictions.

Mary Helen Davis, M.D., associate professor of the University of Louisville School of Medicine, addressed dual diagnoses, including psychiatric disorders and substance abuse, at the 1989 conference. She said detailed studies have found that substance abuse and psychiatric disorders coexist in 20 to 30 percent of cases, and among in-patient populations, the correlation may be as high as 50 percent. "You see these people in the against-medical-advice discharges; they probably consist of about half of the psychiatric emergencies that we see in the emergency room; they're overly represented in terms of accidents and other mishaps; and these are the treatment failures in your chemical dependency programs," she said.

ECONOMIC COSTS

Alcoholism and drug-related disorders exact a tremendously high price on the addict and on the addict's family. In short, the diseases wreck lives. But the economic costs of addiction radiate out far beyond the individual and the extended family, to all of society. And the economic cost of addictions is huge; the numbers are so large that it is difficult to envision them.

The Seventh Special Report to the U.S. Congress on Alcohol and Health estimated that the cost of alcohol abuse and addiction would exceed $150 billion in 1995. Even in a trillion-dollar economy, that is a huge expenditure for the public to bear. The projected cost, based on a study of alcohol's economic costs in 1983, broke down this way: 61 percent of the cost occurs in lost economic productivity and employment, and 13 percent went to health care and treatment.

The cost of drug abuse in 1983 was estimated at almost $60 billion, [17] and its cost has almost certainly soared above $100 billion in the wake of the cocaine explosion. The total bill for abuse and addiction, then, is a mind-boggling $250 billion, and probably moving closer to $300 billion because the estimates were based on 1983 dollars – without the effects of inflation. As the United States struggles to lower the cost of its health system and to compete in a world economy, those are vitally important dollars.

Other studies have found that the money spent on treating alcoholism reduces general health care costs. Untreated alcoholics and their families have significantly higher health costs than nonalcoholics and their families. Moreover, the health costs of recovering alcoholics drops below those of the nonalcoholic families. Two to three years before treatment, the alcoholic's health costs are approximately 130 percent higher than the nonalcoholic; 180 percent higher from 13 months to two years before treatment; and 300 percent higher in the year preceding treatment. "These differences are due primarily to substantially higher inpatient days per month per person for alcoholics," the report to Congress said. [18]

Businesses and the economy sustain losses and unnecessary expense in other ways. Absenteeism is one of the leading warning signs of an addiction, and it has an economic cost. Other expenses include lost-time injuries, wasted time and materiel, and higher insurance costs for both health and workers' compensation.

The risks to the industry are enormous. A backstretch worker at the 1993 Louisville Conference said that, while an active alcoholic, he also had worked as a van driver. "I can remember one day heading for Belmont Park. I had $6-million worth of mares on the truck going up there (from Delaware) to race. I couldn't see the ornament on the hood. I mean, that's real. That's real. That happened," he said.

Sometimes, the potential for loss turns into real, dollar-and-cents losses. Another member of the 1993 panel entitled, "Real People, Real Solutions," said he worked hard while an active alcoholic, was promoted to assistant trainer, and was dispatched from Churchill Downs to Ellis Park with a group of horses. As his drinking became uncontrollable, "everything went to hell. The horses would come up bowed, and I could understand it," he said. "If you don't know what that is, it's a strained ligament up the tendon (of a horse's foreleg); and it was my responsibility to have seen it before it got worse. And I didn't see it until afterwards. It was much worse, and then I had a veterinarian come by to confirm that this horse was bowed. Horses were dehydrated. He (the trainer) would send me two, and I would send two in return back, and those two horses would come back to him 50 to 100 pounds underweight because of my lack of oversight. I wasn't able to recognize that these horses needed more than what I was giving them."

Daniel Perlsweig, a prominent and popular New Jersey trainer who trained 1980 juvenile male champion Lord Avie, said he had an owner bring the issue into sharp focus for him in the early 1960s. For the owner, who had a small trucking line, he claimed a horse for $5,000. Back in the stable area, the horse was being washed by a groom who was an active alcoholic. "And before he reached into the bucket for the sponge, he ran over to his wall box (where a groom keeps his or her brushes and other grooming implements), took a drink, and came back and washed the horse off. Before he scraped him (to remove excess water from the horse's coat), he had to run back and get another drink, come back, scrape the horse off," Perlsweig said at the 1991 Louisville Conference.

The owner asked Perlsweig who would be grooming his $5,000 purchase, and the trainer said it would be the groom who had washed the horse. The owner then gave Perlsweig an insight from his own business. "He said: 'I've got a small trucking line, 50 trucks between Washington and Baltimore. If I just spent $5,000 for a truck, do you think I would let that guy drive it?' " Perlsweig said. "And I thought about it. I said, 'No, I wouldn't.' "

THE PERCEPTION PROBLEM

Well, why do we as an economy and a society – or even as several horse industries – not do something? We put men on the moon; we found a vaccine against polio, and we virtually eradicated smallpox. Surely, we can launch a battle on addictions and save both lives and dollars. Yes, we probably could; but we have not and probably will not until we as a nation begin to look upon addictions as diseases rather than "moral" or "character" shortcomings or, in its more extreme aspects, out-and-out lawlessness. "Historically, alcoholism has been viewed as a moral weakness by the lay public and as an untreatable condition," Sheldon Zimberg, M.D., wrote as recently as 1982. [19]

Christopher Scherf, executive vice president of the Thoroughbred Racing Associations of North America, took note at the 1991 Louisville Conference that, as a group, race track operators are not immune from the perception problem. And he admitted that he too has to catch himself when the perception problem begins to overtake his thinking.

"I don't really understand alcoholism, and I don't think that's uncommon. I just don't understand it as a disease. You know, intellectually I can accept it's a disease; but in my heart, you know, there's a fine line between just self-indulgence or stupidity and addiction," he said. "I see someone tell me about how they almost threw away everything, and they had everything and they threw it away over alcohol, and I have to tell you it's difficult to relate. It's kind of mind-boggling, and I think that's not an uncommon problem.

"I think intellectually most track managers will say and society today will say, 'Yeah, it's a disease.' And then I look at somebody who drinks too much, and I say, 'That guy ought to get a grip on himself and just, you know, straighten up his act,' like it's that simple."

But it is a difficult question that those associated with alcohol and drug abuse programs must address, Scherf said. "The fact is, as diseases go, yours isn't very cute. There's nothing cute about alcoholism or drug addiction. It's not like the March of Dimes or muscular dystrophy where you get poor little kids out there and they just wrench at your heart, and you just would want to do anything you could to help them," he said. "You have the opposite feeling when you see somebody throwing something away. You'd like to help them, but there's also a feeling almost of revulsion there. You know, 'God, how can he do that to himself?' And I mean, I guess that's the thing. People who don't understand it have a difficult time not saying you're doing it to your-self. So that's one of your problems."

Another problem, Scherf said, is that race track operators perceive of themselves as business managers. "Track managers are hired to attend to the bottom line. They're not social workers," Scherf said. "If they wanted to be social workers, they would have gotten out of college and become social workers. They're businessmen. So you have to approach them in that fashion – that this makes good business, economic sense to deal with this."

In this regard, as will become clear in subsequent chapters, executives in the highly traditional business of race track management have not frequently addressed the reality that their most expensive assets, and the assets from which they could develop the greatest productivity and profit gains, are their human resources.

Gary Wilfert, who served as general manager of Turfway Park in Florence, Kentucky, looked into the numbers – how much substance abuse might be costing his track. The disparity between the treatment costs – up to $4,000 for outpatient and $14,000 for inpatient treat-ment per person – and the losses from impaired employees was huge. "I'll take Turfway Park, and we have 450 full-time employees. The national average says that 10 percent of your employees have a sub-stance-abuse problem. I'm going to say, on the race track, even frontside, it's higher. I'm using the number of 15 percent because I just feel that in our industry, it is a higher number than the national average," Wilfert said at the 1991 Louisville Conference. "They're two times more likely to be absent, three times more likely to be late. Those two numbers alone on Turfway Park's payroll would be $65,000 in one year. You usually get two-thirds of the work productivity from someone who has a substance-abuse problem, which on our payroll scale, would cost us approximately $300,000 a year.

"Now, those are numbers that I can give you. Now, when you get down into the workers' comp, that they're five times more likely to file a workers' comp claim," he said. "The problems that you can't put a number on are the other employees, their attitudes, which change when they're working with someone who has these types of problems. Those are all numbers that all add into this figure."

And the total cost for the race track? "Not doing anything is going to cost us a half-million. You don't see it. You don't see it when the balance sheet comes out at the end of the year because they're dark numbers that really aren't there; but the first time, when I looked at this, they are there," Wilfert said. Turfway Park instituted a full-time, on-track treatment program, but unfortunately that program was later discontinued.

Many American businesses and certainly its business-management educators have determined, quantitatively, that the way to save money is to invest in human resources. Often, the race track industry does not follow the examples set by other businesses because it regards itself as unique. In many ways, the industry is not unique, Frank Kuzmits, associate professor of business at the University of Louisville, said in 1990.

"These are common problems. There's nothing unique about the equine industry. There's nothing unique about manufacturing, and there's nothing unique about the university problems. There's nothing unique about the problems down at the bank," he said. "No one is immune to the problem. It's an equal-opportunity illness."

Principally through employee-assistance programs, Kuzmits said, large corporations and some smaller ones have begun to address the issue. "I think the first thing you've got to do is realize that the only way you're going to help anybody with this kind of thing is through rehabilitation. In industry, we learned long ago that if you look the other way or you try to preach and you try to counsel or you pass the problem along to another business or another organization in society, you've really done nothing to really solve that problem. By firing an employee or forcing the employee to quit, you may have in the short-term dealt with your own problem; but that problem still exists.

"We started to get executives to stand up and take notice about rehabilitation when we made it very, very clear that it's profitable. You save money through rehabilitation. And when top-level executives started realizing that, they said, 'Hey, well, maybe. Let's listen and see what you've got to say.' If I can show an executive – and I can go over to the library and pull out research studies that do just this – if I can show an executive that your absenteeism is going to go down and your turnover is going to go down and your health-care costs are going to go down, your grievances are going to go down, your discipline problems are going to go down, and your productivity is going to go up, I mean, you're going to listen," he said.

"And race track owners and managers and farm owners and managers and trainers have got to listen to that message, because we're talking about profits, and your industry knows about profits as well as any industry or company in private industry should."

1. Rabbi Kerry M. Olitzky and Stuart A. Copans, M.D., Twelve Jewish Steps To Recovery (Woodstock, Vermont: Jewish Lights Publishing, 1992).
2. Edgar P. Nace, M.D., The Treatment of Alcoholism (New York: Brunner/Mazel, 1987).
3. Donald W. Goodwin, M.D., Alcoholism (Kalamazoo, Michigan: The Upjohn Company, 1990).
4. Harvey R. St. Clair, Recognizing Alcoholism and Its Effects, A Mini-Guide (Basel, Switzerland, S. Karger AG, 1991).
5. Sheldon Zimberg, M.D., The Clinical Management of Alcoholism (New York: Brunner/Mazel, 1982).
6. Goodwin, Alcoholism, 24.
7. Alcohol and Health, Seventh Special Report to Congress (Rockville, Maryland: U.S. Department of Health and Human Services, 1990).
8. Ibid.
9. Ibid.
10. Ibid.
11. Goodwin, Alcoholism, 16.
12. Alcohol and Health, 22.
13. Nace, Treatment of Alcoholism, 22.
14. St. Clair, Recognizing Alcoholism, 3.
15. Alcohol and Health, 25.
16. St. Clair, Recognizing Alcoholism, 4.
17. Nace, Treatment of Alcoholism, 20.
18. Alcohol and Health, 175.
19. The Clinical Management of Alcoholism, 3

Chapter 3

A Strange Seductive World

If the stable-area workers of North America's race tracks had a theme song, it would be: "We Are Family!" The backstretch areas of the continent's race tracks are exotic, alluring, tight-knit islands where the initiates are treated like family. They are competitors, to be sure, but they are bound together by the race horse – a community of the saddle – and they stick up for one another, as members of any family will. Sometimes, the backstretch community is the worker's only family. And that family offers identity, stature, and cohesiveness. "I'm a racetracker," often is said with pride – and as a challenge, implying that the racetracker has something that the outsider cannot ever have.

But, when the romanticism is stripped away, the world of race-track stable areas has more than a few blemishes. Take away some of the mystique, and the reality is not pretty. The people on the backstretches of North America's race tracks are probably the continent's largest population of working homeless people. Alcohol addictions exist at an alarming rate, more than 30 percent by some estimates, and illegal drugs often are readily available.

Is everyone on the race track homeless? No. Is everyone on the race track poor? No. But a worker who was paid $200 a week in 1980 is still paid $200 more than a decade later, so significant numbers of race-track workers are at or below the poverty level. Is everyone on the race track an alcoholic or drug user? Of course not. But the rates of addiction are startlingly high, and they have been recognized at each Conference on Alcohol and Drug Abuse Programs for the Horse Racing Industry as a significant drag on a horseracing industry that is fighting for its very existence.

No one readily disputes that living conditions on North America's race tracks are poor, if not deplorable. "The newer tracks have nice fireproof dorms and lavatories," trainer Daniel Perlsweig said at the 1991 Louisville Conference. "Some of the sleeping rooms in the older tracks are older than I am, and I slept in them like 40 years ago. I'm sure glad I'm in a helluva lot better shape than they are."

Despite the conditions, horse racing and the world of the stable area – in the unique vernacular of the racetracker, the "backside" – have an undeniable attraction. "It's enticing. It can suck you right in," one counselor said. Perhaps the race track's siren song was best described by William Nack, the award-winning Sports Illustrated senior writer, in his luncheon talk at the 1991 Louisville Conference.

Nack grew up near Arlington Park, now Arlington International Racecourse, and worked there as a teenager. Although he left the backstretch for college, military duty in Vietnam and eventually a distinguished journalism career, he carried away a lifelong love for the sport and the backstretch world. "When I went to work at Arlington in '59, I thought to myself that this was what I wanted to do with my life," he said. "But all of my life I had this wonderful remembrance of my summer-and-a-half or two summers at Arlington, inhaling the sweet and curious rhythms of the race track with its wonderful aromas: hot coffee and fresh doughnuts at 6 a.m., the unguents and balms and salves mixed with the smells of urine and manure, and the tubs of oats and sweet feed cooking in the morning. None of the five corporal senses is tied more closely to the strings on the harp of memory than the sense of smell. And even today, 32 years later, I can still walk into a barn where mash is cooking and feel suddenly transported back to the days of my youth when the days chased each other like kittens chasing their tails.

"That summer of '59 sort of marked the gladdest and damnedest and happiest days of my youth. It was certainly the most memorable three months of my life," he said. "We lived in a single room above the tack room in the summer; and it was wonderful, getting up early in the morning, getting downstairs, walking the horses, finishing work actually at 10 in the morning, when most people are just getting to work down on the Loop, working there throughout the afternoon, grazing horses, being around horses, learning a lot about people. Everybody's got a story on the race track, and one of the wonderful parts about living on the race track was sharing with them – actually listening, at my age.

"At the age of 18, I had very little to say about anything. But listening to an old groom like Slow and Easy, a groom from Calumet Farm, tell stories about Citation and Whirlaway and what life was like in America in the 1930s was just as much a valid education as anything I had ever experienced in school – in fact, a good deal more so. And so I left, I left Arlington; and I left that experience with some very positive feelings."

In 1990 and 1991, Nack went back to the race track and looked into the world of the workers there. He found the good, hard-working people still there – the successors to the grand old race-track workers like Slow and Easy. "I have found a groom at Laurel named Ben Stubbs who sort of became a star of my story. He seemed to me at the time I met him to represent everything that was good about grooms in the field of groom-dom. The reason I liked him so much is because he reminded me of about a thousand other guys I knew and grew up with. His labors were marked by love of the animal and of the sport, and he was doing a lot of this stuff very unselfishly. All of you have met him somewhere. You've all met Ben Stubbs," Nack said.

"I literally would come by the barn unannounced at 6, 7 at night; and there's old Ben on his hands and knees in the stall putting on unguent or Absorbine and working real hard. I met a thousand like him at Arlington years ago; and it was just – he was sort of an inspiration and one of the reasons I fell in love with this business. Eddie Sweat is another, the groom of Secretariat and Riva Ridge. He's out there saying, 'I'm going to win another Derby; I've got to win another Derby' and loves the horse. When you talk to grooms, they love the beast. They love the animal, and it's one of the things that endears you to them because ultimately, they're the center of the business; and somehow the epicenter has sort of gotten lost. You know, the groom and the hotwalker and the people that actually touch the animal have gotten sort of lost."

Indeed, Nack found that the backstretch workers are the people without a name, and sometimes they live in unspeakable conditions.

THE BACKSTRETCH FAMILY

Who are these people? Nack cited the work of John Rosecrance, a widely published sociologist who has studied both the backstretch community and the world of horse-racing gamblers. In simplest terms, Rosecrance said the backstretch workers are the people who do the dirty work of the industry. And, because they do the dirty work, they have the lowest social status on the race track.

The functions of these backstretch populations vary slightly from industry to industry, but they are similar at every North American race track. At the bottom of the totem pole, at the very bottom rung of the social ladder, is the hotwalker. What does a hotwalker do? He or she walks hots, meaning horses that have completed their daily exercise. After a routine gallop, a horse will be walked counterclockwise for 30 minutes in the barn's covered aisles – known as a "shedrow" – while the animal is "watered off," meaning that the horse replenishes body fluids by drinking from a bucket hung in the shedrow. After a workout – a faster gallop around the track at or near racing speed – the horse will be walked for 45 minutes or more. Hotwalkers are paid only a few dollars for each horse, and the timing is such that six or so horses effectively constitute a maximum number of paid strolls around the shedrow each morning.

Other than a gentle but strong right arm – hotwalkers always walk to the left of their charges – and a talent for avoiding the horse's hooves, this task requires little skill, and the work is easy to find. Paul Berube, president of the Thoroughbred Racing Protective Bureau, described the most common employment process at the 1991 Louisville Conference. "We have a group of prospective stable employees gathered outside the stable gate while the security guard or stable gate man announces their availability and presence to the trainers in the stable area – basically telling them, if you need someone, come on out and get them," he said. In another variant, the job seeker will be granted a day pass and will go around in the morning to solicit a job in one of the stables. "Usually it works," Berube said. "Someone is hired, and then we get into the licensing sequence, which, as we know, is a function of state racing commissions or licensing authorities." Because horse racing is in essence the conduct of an activity that otherwise would be illegal – public gambling – all race-track workers must be licensed by state agencies.

If the hotwalker shows some promise or merely sticks around for several weeks, he or she most likely will be trained to be a groom, who is the caretaker of the horse. In the Standardbred industry and in some Thoroughbred operations, the hotwalker position has been eliminated, and the groom takes responsibility of all day-to-day care of the race horse. This is a position that requires diligence, skill at animal husbandry, and a bucketful of patience. Working six or even seven days a week, the groom shows up at 5 or 5:30 a.m. to prepare his or her horses – three or more – for the day's exercise. They groom their horses, put the tack – saddle, bridle, and any other equipment – on them, and clean out the stalls while the horses are galloping. When the horse returns, they take the animal into the stall while the tack is removed and, if weather permits, wash down the horse with the assistance of a hotwalker. The groom finishes the stall clean-up while the horse walks and also gets the next horse ready for exercise. After the horses are cooled down, the groom rubs and bandages the legs – both to prevent injury in the stall and to provide support for the vitally important legs after exercise.

In the argot, grooms will not say that they groom or take care of a horse. Typically, they will say that they "rub" a horse, a reference to the now largely abandoned practice of rubbing a horse's coat (with a "rub rag") to promote circulation. When a horse is entered in a race, the groom will walk the horse from the backstretch to the paddock area where the horses are saddled. In the vernacular, that is known as "running" the horse. For the better part of two decades, grooms have worked for $200 a week, plus 1 percent of their horses' earnings. Even if a groom's horses earn $1-million, the annual compensation would be $10,400 in salary and $10,000 in bonuses. And that would be a very good year. Some trainers offer health insurance, but they are rarities, and few tracks offer health plans for backstretch workers. In terms of health insurance, most stable workers go without coverage for all of their time on the race track.

Still, grooms invariably have a fervent attachment to the horse, to the sport, and to the backstretch community. "He works on this horse seven days a week; he sleeps and lives with horses; he smells like horses. His life is horses," said Bernard Flint, a leading Kentucky trainer, at the 1989 Louisville Conference. "When he leads that $2,500 or $3,500 nag over there (to race), to him that is the most important thing in this whole world, to win that race. No matter who they are. I don't even care if they're a hotwalker. They all walk proud. And if you ever go there and watch at the finish line, I'll show you the happiest people in the world when they win a race."

Another skill position on the backstretch is the exercise rider. They are usually paid more than $10 per horse, which means that they can make a decent living if they do not get hurt. A fall often means no work with no workers' compensation, and no health coverage. The exercise riders are drawn from several sources. Some are show riders who are valued with their skill on a horse's back; others are aspiring jockeys who, in many cases, have worked as a hotwalker or groom before being allowed to ride a horse; others are former jockeys whose skills have eroded with age or whose weight has risen beyond 115 or 116 pounds, which is effectively the upper limit for jockeys. Although jockeys often are not considered to be part of the back-stretch culture, they in fact come out of the backside world and often re-enter it at the end of their careers. In addition, jockeys and their agent make their rounds of the backstretch in the mornings, often riding horses for workouts in the hope that the jockey will have the mount the next time the horse races.

Grooms who succeed at their jobs can progress to stable foreman or assistant trainer. As they do so, the better ones hone their people skills in hopes that some day they will become a trainer, who is the person retained by an owner and given ultimate responsibility for the horse's well-being and racing success. With some exceptions – prin-cipally those horse people like Billy Turner who came out of steeple-chasing – the trainer and the stable employees are all products of the backstretch culture. Lori Weinegar, who worked as a counselor at Philadelphia Park and at several New Jersey tracks, said "the barns represented a miniature family, with the trainers usually acting as par-ents, and really set up very hierarchically like that. In that there was a family in each barn, there were also helpers in every barn, and there were good guys and bad guys, the scapegoat children, and the hero children, and all that kind of stuff."

What kind of people are they? They are people like any other people, like members of society generally. They are, in general, good people, but there are some bad people, and many sick people. "Some of the people on the backside are very, very dedicated, and they do influence people for the better side," trainer Danny Perlsweig said at the 1991 Louisville Conference. "The drunks and the druggies also influence people, and they drag them down. Alcohol and drugs are readily accessible. We all know that. They're not only at the race track; they're all over. We have to find some way to stop it or slow it down."

THE BACKSTRETCH SOCIETY

While members of these stable families ostensibly are competitors, they invariably will close ranks against the outside world. For many in this society, their insularity is their identity.

"This is the population, and the single most salient characteristic of the population you're working with and for is their isolation from the outside world," Bill Nack told counselors and others at the 1991 Louisville Conference. "They don't exist. It's like they've all been taken prisoner and put behind this moat. And, except for people like you and a few others who really care about them and are ministering to them and trying to find out what their needs are, they're back there doing it on their own, and they're isolated. The psychiatrists say they are classic candidates for drug and alcohol abuse because of their loneliness, because of the kind of isolated life they lead."

John Mayton, former director of the Winners Foundation, noted at the 1989 Louisville Conference that the backside really has no secrets. "It's a competitive society, everybody competes against everybody else, and one of the ways to put yourself at risk is to reveal one of your weaknesses. And if someone would just perhaps see me going into the Winners Foundation trailer to go to one of those Alcoholics Anonymous meetings, they'd know I was a drunk, and that's a real scary thing for me to do. Especially if I'm a trainer or a groom or a jockey, because everybody is going to know. Well, the truth is, everybody knows anyhow. I mean, it's not like my drug and alcohol use was a secret in the community," Mayton said. "The only person who doesn't really know it's a problem is the guy that's got the problem or the gal that's got the problem."

Bob Babes, who was the counselor at the Maryland tracks in the 1980s, chronicled both the isolation and the attitudes of the backstretch worker. The backstretch, he said in 1989, constitutes "a system that is, in social-work terms, enmeshed. It's real guarded, it's a system in which people tend to live, they tend to work, and they tend to socialize together; they do all these things together. There are not many industries that I have worked in, or known people to work in, that exist that way. When you have all of that, ideally, you could have really a supportive system, where people could help each other. That didn't really happen, or that doesn't exist in Maryland anyway. Maybe in some tracks it does.

"It's prime territory for I guess the term could be enabling," he said. "People tend to protect each other back there. They tend to want to be the care-givers of themselves; they tend to want to not allow others to know what others are doing unless you are a racetracker."

Babes needed almost a year to penetrate the system – his presence and visibility helped, as did the endorsement of racetrackers who had received help through him. "To penetrate this closed system, you need to be real, and you need to be genuine. And you need to be careful not to be too real and too genuine," he told other counselors at the first Louisville Conference in 1989. "I think there's a fine line there. You start trying to overrun these people with love and affection, and they aren't going to go for it. They don't know what love and affection are, the vast majority of them."

Babes also discovered that the stable workers, despite the defensive claims of uniqueness, did not really feel good about themselves. "It's a feeling inside of them that they're carny people," he said. "These people have a philosophy of 'blame the victim.' They feel victimized. They feel, basically, that they're just backsiders." With more than one client, Babes had a conversation like this: "They'll bring up: 'Hey, Bob, you know why these fences are here?' I say: 'So patrons can't sneak in.' 'No Bob, the fences are here not to keep people out. The fences are here to keep us in.' They believe that. There are lots of people on the race track that believe that's why the fences are there. They laugh and giggle, but hey, I've worked with enough defense mechanisms to know that laughs and giggles can mean a lot more than just laughs and giggles."

Babes also found that the race track nicknames often reflected feel-ings of inferiority. "They have all these weird-ass names. It pisses me off, and I tell them so, that they're not that way. And I try and let them know that there's goodness in there, and we'll work toward the goodness," he said. "And many of these people on the backside of the race tracks, their insides are tarnished, believe me. . . . they're sitting there inside going, you know: 'I'm no good; I'm a bum. I make a hundred bucks a week, broke two days after I got it. And this is the way I am, and this is the way the race track is.' And that's the way they think; they believe that they're different from the outside world. And I think it goes with blame the victim."

The race track environment also offers a hiding place for those who are disaffected from society generally – because of their substance abuse or for other reasons. "It's a safe haven, the race track," Larry Wheeler, executive director of the Oregon Horsemen's Benevolent and Protective Association in 1989, said at that year's Louisville Conference. "Once they get in there, they're safe. Nobody's really going to bother them. Lots of people live there the whole race meet; they don't get off those grounds. A lot of them don't have licenses. Once they can sneak in there, they're safe. Nobody really bothers them unless they cause a disturbance."

Race track people often are grateful to those outsiders – such as counselors and chaplains – who recognize them as individuals, who refuse to treat them as invisible. "It's really not hard to make friends at the race track. Whatever you give them, man, they just suck it up. They just take it, and it means so much to them," Lori Weinegar said at the 1989 Louisville Conference. "I give poker chips out, just like they do at A.A. I give out poker chips to my clients. I have these lit-tle stars, and I put them on them for when they go to meetings, or when they get more time sober, and things like that. I give them the chips and I tell them: 'Look, you hold on to this chip. I'll tell you what, when you feel like drinking or drugging, you just reach into your pocket, you hold on to that chip, and that chip is going to help keep you clean.'

"I thought this was a really cool thing that we were doing here. But you always have to carry it in your pocket. But what would happen was, they would come into my office. Maybe they've been doing real good work, or they went to three meetings that week, and I want to put this star on their chip, and they wouldn't have their chip. The chip would be in their room. What I learned was that they wouldn't carry their chips around because they were so valuable. It became such a valuable commodity, and it became competitive between them, who had the most stars. This was the big thing, who had the most stars. Some of them would try to worm more chips out of me than just one. The little poker chip became so meaningful that they keep them in their rooms, and I have to carry the stars around in my truck now so that I can make house calls and give stars out," she said. "The smallest thing is so important to them."

A SICK FAMILY

In his work at the Maryland tracks, Babes also found that alcohol was enmeshed in the enmeshed environment. "I was there about 18 months, and I went to the (Maryland racing) commission, and I said: 'Hey, these people are all drinking.' Every day, I walk through the barn area. I don't want to be real weird about this, but almost every barn, you can find somebody with a beer. At 7, 8 o'clock in the morning. I've had many jobs in my life, and many jobs warranted drinking at 8 o'clock in the morning, but we couldn't do it. You'd get fired; you'd lose your job. But on the race track, it's okay," he said at the 1989 conference.

"Another thing about the alcohol is that it's a reward system on the race track. Owners, trainers, jocks, they win a race, they win a stake, they win a big allowance race, two or three cases of beer will come to the shedrow. Three quarts of vodka will come to the shedrow. Happens all the time. So what we're fighting here is not just the working staff having an alcohol problem. What we're fighting here is alcoholism as an institution within an institution. It's an institution on the race track. That's how bizarre it is."

The drinking is facilitated by some backstretch kitchens, where beer is sold – and bought – at all hours of the day. Several race-track treatment programs, however, have successfully stopped this practice. Babes, in his time on the track, found at least two instances of illegal activity involving alcohol. "There are bootleggers on the race track. They drive around with their little cars and they open their trunk, and they have beer, and they have wine and alcohol. It's sort of like that crack house thing; they have it in their car. And they'll drive around to the barns, and they'll sell it," he said. At one of the Maryland tracks during his time there, Babes said, "there's a place that you go from the backside to the frontside, and you have to walk past the guard. And when you walk past the guard, he goes: 'Budweiser?' Now, the first time I walked by him, I thought: 'Budweiser?' So I didn't know what the heck he was doing, so I just kept walking. So one of my clients came in, and I asked him. He says, yeah, the guy sells beer and he's a guard, supposed to check the badges going through." Babes said that, in his time at the Maryland tracks, he was able to get the beer out of the track kitchens and crack down on the bootleggers on wheels.

The alcohol and drugs do more than create a sick environment; they foster a dangerous and violent milieu. Gary Wilfert, general manager of Turfway Park in Boone County, Kentucky, in 1992, checked out the statistics on police calls to the track, both the back-stretch and the grandstand, which is known as the "frontside" in race-track parlance. He was floored by the numbers. "In 1989, 67 percent of the arrests – they had to come to Turfway Park and arrest someone – were drug- or alcohol-related. In 1990, it was 54 percent; and in 1991, it was a staggering 75 percent," he said.

Paul Berube, the Thoroughbred Racing Protective Bureau president, also found some anecdotal evidence. While traveling to the 1990 Louisville Conference, he looked through the reports in his briefcase. "I must have looked at about 30 or 40 reports, just things that I do on a daily basis," he said. "And in those 30 or 40 reports, there were 10 situations that either involved alcohol, disorderly types, drug arrests, drug use, or drug-testing program penalties that were imposed. So 10 out of those reports that I saw and read pertain to security situations."

AN ENABLING FAMILY

Because members of the backstretch community are so protective of their own, they are big-time candidates for enabling behavior. This, Dr. Robert Frierson said at the 1989 Louisville Conference, is distinctly a family problem. "This is another way that the families try to avoid the pain. They cover up for the patient's addiction. They'll call the boss and say he's sick; they'll get a doctor's excuse when he really is just drunk; they'll do all kinds of things as a way of covering up for his addiction," he said.

"And these are some of the patterns of enabling behavior: Avoiding and shielding; attempting to control – you know, making bargains, or threats – 'If you don't stop using drugs, I'm going to leave you.' And then usually the threat is not carried out, so the patient begins to minimize it. Withholding sex, buying the abuser things to divert his attention, staying with him 24 hours a day, keeping vigils. We've had people who were doing that – taking over responsibilities for the abuser, rationalizing and accepting the use, even cooperating and collaborating with the use. And rescuing – trying to rescue the person – and subserving one's own needs."

One of the principal enablers – and often an unwitting or unwitting one – is the paterfamilias, the trainer, who will overlook unacceptable behavior as long as the work gets done. Bernard Hettel, executive director of the Kentucky Racing Commission in the 1990s and chief state steward at Kentucky's tracks in 1989, had an acute awareness of this fact when he spoke before the first Louisville Conference. Then on the backstretch of Kentucky's race tracks each day, he noted that he had "a lot of walk-in trade, if you will, every day. Certainly, I'm very aware. I'm not in some ivory tower," he said. "We have rules right now that prohibit intoxication and drug addiction. And certainly enforcement of those rules is a difficulty. Part of that difficulty is the tolerance of the participants on the backside, primarily the owners and trainers who tolerate their employees, the stable people, grooms, exercise boys, hotwalkers. It's fine for that guy to drink all day as long as he's sound in the morning to walk the horse, or rub the horse, or clean up the horse. That, to me, is the major problem."

Lori Weinegar also said that she had encountered difficulties arising from trainers' need to have people to do the day's work. "I had a situation where I had two clients, a girlfriend and a boyfriend, both of whom were involved in drugs and alcohol. The boyfriend, I sent him to rehab on the condition that when he came back he could work on the track, but he could no longer live on the race track. While he was gone, I tried to send his lover to a regular program, but

I got so much static from her trainer that I had to compromise, and I could only send her to a detox, and she went in for seven days. I got a lot of static from her trainer because she was 'only' an alcoholic. She wasn't a drug addict, and, after all, drug addicts steal and alcoholics just drink, and as long as they show up for work, that's what counts," Weinegar said. "I really had to fight for this young lady to go to detox, and off the site to go to rehab."

Focusing on the short-term concerns, such as having a groom for that week or that month, often subverts trainers' long-term needs. "Trainers who care do make a difference," Danny Perlsweig said. "We have less turnover and much better help. I've had some people with me for more than 20 years. One old fellow has rubbed every good horse I've ever had, and like it's a pleasure to be around him." He is, in fact, a groom in the finest tradition of the sport.

A Neglected Family

Perlsweig mentioned that the keepers of million-dollar horses are housed in hovels or accommodations so spare that they are indistinguishable from a jail cell — except that they have less natural light than a jail cell, no running water, and no toilet facilities. "It would be nice to move them up to a better living condition," he said. Jim Ryan's efforts in Maryland also have stressed life-style and living conditions, which also were a principal focus of Bill Nack's 1991 story in Sports Illustrated. One difference from his time at Arlington, Nack said, was that part-time accommodations now are occupied year-round.

"Race tracks in those days were really itinerant circuses. The stables picked up every 30 to 60 days and moved from places like Arlington Park to Washington Park to Hawthorne to Sportsman's," Nack said. "And it began to occur to me that this itinerant population had certain advantages, and it became sort of obvious to me when I started reading — researching this story. One of the reasons is that in places such as Pimlico and Laurel, where Jim Ryan has done some research of his own and some work, the race track housing was built for 30-day and 60-day stays, and so was Belmont Park, and so was Aqueduct, and so were most of the tracks up north.

"And so I found a situation when I went into Laurel, for instance, where grooms were living year-round in housing that was designed for spring meet, fall meet, summer meet particularly. There was no running water. There were no toilet facilities in individual rooms; and people basically, if they got up at 3 in the morning on a January day and had to go to the washroom, they had to get dressed and walk outside, walk about 150 yards through the snow and the sleet, whatever was happening. And I happened to be there when it was snowing a lot. I was there in late December, early January; and I began to get another perspective on life on the backstretch, and it made me think that this is not what it was when I grew up. Times had changed."

One thing that has not changed, however, was that the person placed in substandard housing often is blamed for the conditions. In short, blame the victim. After his story appeared, Nack was pulled aside by a prominent New York trainer. "He said, 'You know, I remember 20 years ago . . .' – You know what I'm going to say, don't you? – 'Twenty years ago I had a little housing unit here at Belmont; and I fixed it up, put curtains up and everything, you know.' And I'm going, 'Uh huh, uh huh, here it comes.' 'And you know what? They weren't in it for five weeks, and they ruined it.'

"Well, it struck me that this was the same appeal, the same kind of case that the Bronx slumlord makes to the magistrate when he's called up on charges of failing to provide decent living conditions for his tenants. You've read the old saw in the newspaper accounts: 'Well, Judge, if I fix up the place and make it livable, they'll only destroy it.' The situation to this extent is classic. The victim becomes the perpetrator. He's the one to blame; and hence in that passing the blame, there is a giving up, a yielding of responsibility. That's basically the end product," he said. "I think that the Jockey Club or some group could fit it in between its laminitis studies to actually study about people on the backstretch and to find out what makes them tick and what they need. It's an old syndrome, and I'm calling it the institutionalized maintenance of the invisible man because there's a certain vested and economic interest in those who would say, 'No, we don't need to help these people.' I mean, it's going to cost some money."

One relatively inexpensive method of reducing the isolation of the backstretch community is special recreational and educational programs, and many race tracks have undertaken those activities in recent years. "We need more counseling and classes; and we need more activities, such as ball games, movies, barbecue, hobby classes, whatever it takes to do this," Danny Perlsweig said in 1991. "I remember years ago at Atlantic City Race Course when it was in its heyday, one Sunday every summer, they had what they called the Jocks Agents' Picnic. I don't know whether anybody remembers that." Well, Danny Perlsweig certainly did. He listened to the conference speakers, shared their concerns, and remembered the old jocks' agent picnics. The following year, he launched the first Backstretch Appreciation Day at Monmouth Park. With the support of the track and track vendors, Danny Perlsweig's brainchild has becoming a highly successful annual event.

FATAL ASSUMPTIONS

Race tracks are renowned for their rumors, an amazing number of which turn out to be utterly and totally false. The backstretch has its share of verities, and many of them are utterly false. At the worst, they are fatal assumptions. Take, for instance, the trainer who was asked why an impaired jockey had received so many mounts. The trainer said he would not be bothered that a jockey was using drugs or alcohol because those substances "don't affect some people." Clearly, the trainer had made an assumption about human biology that was incorrect and quite possibly fatal. Would he have suggested that gasoline, when ignited, would not affect "some people"? Certainly not. Would he suggest that a deadly poison like cyanide would not affect "some people"? No. But he stated as an absolute truth that "some people" could somehow resist the effects of alcohol and drugs. He was absolutely wrong, and perhaps dead wrong.

The trainer offered perhaps an even more dangerous fatal assumption. He suggested that drugs can improve human performance. Certainly, some jockeys will say that they "rode harder" while impaired, but that was because the substance had dulled the jock's sense of reasonable risk. As one jockey said: "Cocaine made me numb."

The truth is very different from the trainer's fatal assumption. Drugs, alcohol, and human chemistry follow standard rules of biology. In carefully controlled experiments, for example, highly skilled airplane pilots appeared to do all right while flying intoxicated but, when their skill was most needed, they made mistakes that would have killed them and others. Many tried to land their aircraft 200 feet short of the designated runway while believing all the time that they were doing fine.

For some time, the horseracing industry has been making a similarly fatal assumption: that the conditions of the backstretch, with its widespread abuse of alcohol and drugs as well as deplorable living quarters, are someone else's problem. The racing commissions have looked to the tracks, and the tracks have looked to the trainers, and some trainers have responded positively. But other trainers have bounced the problem back to the tracks, some of which have responded admirably to improve conditions and reduce impairments – principally through establishing substance-abuse programs with matching funds from the Ryan Family Foundation in 1989 and 1990. In many cases, the horse owners – the people whose investments are in the hands of impaired backstretch workers – have stated implicitly or explicitly that they want nothing to do with racing's addiction problems. In so many words, these owners have said that they don't want to be bothered.

Lyle Sussman, a University of Louisville business professor who co-led a session at the 1990 Louisville Conference, said eloquently that the crisis situation represents a failure of leadership. "I've looked at this problem in manufacturing and other service organizations for a long time, and let me say this. Nothing is going to happen unless leadership comes from the top," he said. "If you do nothing, it's business as usual. It's the accidents. It's the injuries. It's the absenteeism. It's the turnover. It's the drug dealing and the other problems that you have on the backstretch at every track in the country. So at some point in time, you've got to break the cycle; and that comes from top leadership.

"And if you want to get people to listen to you, at the top or at the middle or at the bottom, you talk bottom line. You talk money. You talk profits, and you talk about winning horse races. And the way you do that is with competent people, and competent people are people who are not abusing drugs or alcohol. It's as simple as that."

Chapter 4

East Side, West Side

John Giovanni, a former jockey and national manager of the Jockeys' Guild since the mid-1980s, has been a stalwart advocate of strong but compassionate measures against alcohol and drug abuse in the horseracing industry. Giovanni, however, does not want his members singled out for drug testing, and he opposes random testing, in part because he believes it does not work and also because he suspects that jockeys would become the most accessible subjects for random testing.

He also told a story at the 1991 Conference on Alcohol and Drug Abuse Programs in the Horse Racing Industry that illustrated how problems of substance abuse penetrate all parts of the industry. While at a race track, Giovanni noticed that some employees of the track's food concessionaire – the people who serve the meals and dispense hot dogs, beer, and sodas at the stands – were going around the facility and picking discarded beer cups out of trash containers. This, Giovanni thought, was very peculiar behavior, so he watched them. They took the beer cups back to the concession stands, rinsed them out, and then sold beer in them again.

Protecting the environment may be one thing, Giovanni thought, but this beer-cup recycling was going a bit far. Indeed it was well out of bounds. "The reason they were doing this was because the beer was in a keg form, and they sold the beer and charged by the cup," Giovanni said at the 1991 Louisville Conference. "If a hundred cups were dropped off at that stand and a hundred cups were sold, then X amount of dollars was supposed to be in the till. What these people were doing is recycling the cups, and they were selling cups with lipstick on them and all this, and it was an absolute disgrace. But come to find out, the people who were doing this had a serious drug problem. They had a cocaine problem. They were doing this for extra money, for cash." The concession employees thus were able to keep all the money from the "recycled" cups because their financial responsibility was based on the number of new cups they sold.

Clearly, alcohol and drug problems are not limited to the backstretch. They extend to the jocks' room, to be sure, but they also are found in the pari-mutuel department, in the maintenance department, in the food stands – and even in the executive suite. As has been said more than once, addictions are equal-opportunity diseases, and they can affect those on the entry levels of the race track economy, those who suddenly find their income growing substantially (such as young jockeys), and those who have reached the highest levels of the industry. John Samerjan, a New Jersey Sports and Exposition Authority official, said at the 1990 Louisville Conference that Meadowlands Race Track, in East Rutherford across the Hudson River from New York City, had instituted an employee-assistance program for its frontside – as distinguished from the backside – workers.

These employees were in the admissions department, security, parking, mutuels – in short, every department coming in contact with the race track's patrons. These are the people who, by their demeanor and conduct, determine whether the track's patrons have an enjoyable time or are turned off by the race-track experience. More than horse trainers and track executives, these people hold the future of horse racing in their hands.

In the first year and a half of the Meadowlands' employee-assistance program, "97 of our employees availed themselves of the service. Of that number, over one-third were referred for alcohol and drug in-patient or out-patient counseling," he said in October 1990. "Those 97 referrals represent 11 percent of our full-time work force seeking help in the first year of the program. In the second year, it is still going along at about 7 or 8 percent. I'll leave the math to you for what that would mean in your own office. And we don't pretend we are reaching all our employees who need help."

The statistics are compelling, and certainly the Meadowlands experience is by no means an aberration. The problems are there, on the backstretch, in the jocks' room, in the board room, in the grandstand, in society generally. But the Meadowlands and other programs are evidence that progress can and will be made, that lives will be saved. Sobriety has saved the lives and careers of many people, and the stories of two well-known figures in the horseracing world are worth repeating. They were succeeding in their fields while heading for disaster; they were, in effect, working their way up to bottom, that moment where they surrendered to recovery. One was helped by a touch of the Almighty, and the other through a 12-step program. Here are their stories.

PAT'S STORY

Patrick Day is one of the most skillful and successful jockeys ever to sit astride a horse. He has ridden a Kentucky Derby winner, Preakness Stakes winners, Belmont Stakes winners, and he has ridden two victors in the Breeders' Cup Classic. From the start, he was a natural – that individual with all the skills. He also was, it turned out, a world-class drinker and drug abuser. But, in a motel room more than a decade ago, Pat Day met his God and changed his life – irreversibly – forever.

A native of Golden, Colorado, Day first took up rodeo, riding bulls in a world that also has its share of problems with substance abuse, and became a professional jockey when he was 19. Day's parents had taught him about the dangers inherent in alcohol and drugs, but – like many children who deeply love their parents – he did not pay quite enough attention to that message. "I had started drinking when I was about 16 or 17," he said, and attributed his alcohol use to peer pressure. "I felt that drinking was the 'in' thing to do, and so that's what I'd done. When I came on the race track, of course, the accessibility to other things was more available to me. It started with marijuana and graduated from there, if I recall correctly, to pills, speed – white crosses, we called them at the time – and of course, from there it was just a short step to cocaine. In the midst of all this, of course, I was still indulging in alcohol, because, after all, that was legal," he said. "I was 19, and Arizona was one of the few states that allowed you to sit at the counter and buy hard liquor at 19."

Day and the racing world quickly found out that his skills were extraordinary. "I was blessed with a tremendous amount of natural ability. The way that I came on the race track and my quick-rising success all lent credence to this. I was a short six months galloping horses on the farm and working on the race track before I started riding. That's basically unheard of. When I first was working on the farm, they had told me that I should anticipate being on the farm for two to three years before I ever looked at a race track and then working for somebody at the race track for another year or two before I started riding. This was in January of 1973; in July of 1973, I was riding races.

"In December or January of that next year, I was leading rider at Turf Paradise in Phoenix, Arizona. Turf Paradise is not a top-class race meet, but in the winter time it's a very tough meeting. For somebody to not have been around any longer than I was and to do that good was pretty phenomenal," he said. "My new-found and quickly found success caused me to have what you might consider a big head. I started walking to the beat of my own drum; I felt that I was God's gift to the race track." Money filled his pockets, and he suddenly found himself in company with people who lived in the fast lane. "My desire to be part of that crowd led me to become more and more involved in the drugs and the alcohol," he said.

Day eventually took his success to New York, which is filled with jockeys possessing extraordinary talents. He did poorly for a while, then started riding winners. When he first arrived in New York in the mid-1970s, Day was not using alcohol or drugs regularly. "As I started making it and started doing well, of course, I felt like it was time to celebrate and break out the drugs and get involved in the alcohol again." A marriage failed, and "I wanted to blame the race track for my heartache, for my problems, the pain that I was going through," Day said. "I went to Florida and went on what I would seriously consider a self-destructive trip. I went down there, I thought I would try to ride for a while, but my mind was not in it. And there was one stint for about eight or ten days that I have absolutely no recall."

A Pennsylvania-based horseman, Steve Rowan, helped Day to get straightened out for a time, and the young jockey caught fire in New Orleans. Rowan, he said, "took the necessary steps to get me back to the race track, helped to get me straightened out. He got me to New Orleans, where we started riding – he was acting as my agent at the time. He kind of rekindled that fire in me. He helped me to see and to realize that I really loved riding races, I loved doing what I was doing, and it was what I was really meant to do."

Day's career blossomed, and he took Chicago's Arlington Park by storm in 1978. "Once I got to Chicago and started doing good, here come the drugs again," he said. Day married his current wife, Sheila, in 1979, and he noted that they have been through some tough times together. "In the midst of all of this, I had a few run-ins with the law. And because of the financial resources – because of the money that I had, because of the position I was in – I was able to get out of it. And I don't know that that was really so good. I sometimes think that possibly it had been better if . . . you want to dance, you got to pay the fiddler. Maybe I should have paid the fiddler. At any rate, I didn't, and I continued with my wicked lifestyle."

He also continued to ride in championship form. In 1982, he was the country's leading rider by victories after a season-long struggle with Angel Cordero Jr. "We arrived at Churchill Downs in November, the gentleman came through selling cocaine, and I went over and bought some. Why I sought not to get into it at the time, I don't know, but I put it away and continued to ride through November and December. The last day of the year came down to a tie between Angel Cordero and myself. I was able to get transportation to Delta Downs in the southwestern corner of Louisiana. I went down there, I rode two races and won two races and secured the title," he said.

"I came back to New Orleans and for probably three or four or five days, indulged in the white powder. Now that was, in that mindset that I was presently in, that was the way that I felt like I was supposed to celebrate," Day said. "We went to Las Vegas I was doing so much coke that invariably I'd be sitting at the table playing cards in Vegas and my nose would just start running. I think I spent more time in the bathroom trying to get my nose to stop than I did actually playing cards or enjoying Las Vegas."

Still, something was incomplete in Day's life. He and his wife vacationed in Hawaii early in 1984, and they attended Sunday services there. Perhaps that was the spark that ignited the fire. On January 27, Day flew to Miami to ride a horse for a friend, Claude R. "Shug"

McGaughey III, in a stakes race at Hialeah Park. "When I was all ready for bed, I sat down and was watching what was on TV, and it was Jimmy Swaggart; he had a televised crusade. And even searching as I knew I was, I didn't feel that what he had to offer was what I was looking for. And I had this feeling about Christianity or about God, I felt like that was for women and children and wimps, and I didn't feel like I fell into any of those categories; certainly didn't want to be considered a wimp, anyway. And thought I could go it alone," Day said.

"I went through the stations changing channels. There wasn't anything that really got my attention. And so I turned the TV set off and laid down. It was unusual that I fell right to sleep in view of the fact that, well, there were those frequent times when I would have had a drink or two. But this time, I hadn't had a drink for a couple of days. And when I laid down, I fell immediately into a deep sleep, so deep, as a matter of fact, that when I awoke some time later, I thought I'd been sleeping all night, I'd slept so soundly. But I woke to the distinct feeling that I was no longer by myself, and I sat up by the bed and I looked around, trying to put my finger on what it was that I was feeling. I couldn't see anything. So I got up and I turned the TV set back on; I don't know to this day if I was directed to do that or if I'd done that in an attempt to rid myself of these feelings. But any rate, I turned the TV set on. And I realized immediately that, though I felt that I'd been sleeping a long time, in fact I hadn't been sleeping long at all. Jimmy Swaggart was still on TV; he had just completed bringing his message of salvation for the congregation and to those that were watching by television, and he was having an altar call.

"And in that instant, I knew that that was the Lord Jesus there with me. And I knew that I was being given a choice: That I could either commit my life to Him, accept Him into my life, receive the forgiveness of my sins and live a worthwhile life, or I could continue living in the world as I was. There was no decision to be made. I just fell on my face right there before the TV set and I wept, cried, and confessed that I was a sinner, lost, struggling in this lonely world, and that I needed Jesus in my heart. I don't know how long I laid on the floor. I do know that we did win the race the next day," he said.

On the flight back home to Colorado, Day realized that he no longer wanted alcohol; the very thought of it nauseated him. "I knew at that instant, at that moment, that the Lord had delivered me from that, and I have not, praise God, since then had any desire to get involved; I've had no relapse, no temptation. I've had struggles in other areas of my life but, praise God, I've had no problem with the drugs and the alcohol," he said.

For Day, his faith was the answer; a belief in God also and a reliance on a Higher Power are major components of the 12 steps in Alcoholics Anonymous and programs based on its principles. But the Hall of Fame jockey also realizes that his way – his blessing – will not be available to everyone. Drug and alcohol programs, he said at the 1989 Louisville Conference, offer a road to recovery for those who have not been touched by a religious experience. In the middle years of the 1990s, Pat Day stands as an example of everything that is right about Thoroughbred racing. He is a winner among winners.

The Jockeys' Guild Inc. – Day is a member and has served as the organization's treasurer – also has been striving to help members to avoid alcohol and drug dependencies. The Guild's approach brooks no nonsense. Day, Giovanni, and others know that one error by anyone in the complex cycle of getting a horse into a race – a mistake by a groom, a trainer, an exercise rider, or an assistant starter – can put a jockey at risk of injury or death. Moreover, Giovanni said, "I don't think I could begin to tell you what it's like to sit in the starting gate and look over at somebody who's staring up in space. It's a dangerous enough business as it is, and we don't want people out there who are not in charge of their faculties." Still, the Jockeys' Guild position recognizes, first, that addictions are a disease and, second, that intervention often leads to recovery.

"The Jockeys' Guild has taken the position that the first time somebody comes up with a positive, he should be sent up for an evaluation so at least we know what we're dealing with," said Giovanni, who served as chair of the American Horse Racing Federation's Committee on Substance Abuse. "This guy or girl – is this person a first-time user, smoking marijuana; or is this person heavily into crack? Is this person drinking a quart of scotch a day or, you know, what exactly are we dealing with here? And I don't think you can do that without a professional evaluation."

If the condition is regarded as an addiction, treatment is necessary, of course. If it is not considered to be an addiction, the individual should be counseled and allowed to resume participation in the industry if he or she agrees to regular testing, "be that once a day, twice a day, once a week, once a month, whenever," Giovanni said. "In our opinion, this helps to keep people on their toes. They don't know if they're going to be tested. They don't – they're not sure when it's going to come. They're not sure that if before the first race they have to give a test, and they might have to give another one after the fifth."

For a second positive, the Jockeys' Guild supports a suspension of at least six months and mandatory treatment. "For a third positive, we don't think they should be in the business any longer. It's a pretty stiff penalty, pretty tough thing to do," Giovanni said. "People have to know that they're either going to have to face their problem or they shouldn't be involved in a business where they're putting other people's lives at risk."

PETE'S STORY

If Peter Drypolcher suffered from any deficiency, it was that he lacked deficiencies. Things in life came easily. Tall, good-looking, bright, and popular, he was president of his high school student body in El Paso, Texas, and he was headed toward an equally outstanding career at Texas Western College. When he entered the racing game, the calculus of the horse-racing industry was an open book for him.

If someone had walked up to him as he left Austin High at age 17 and told him that over the next 16 years he would become a hopeless alcoholic, "I would have thought they were the stupidest person I'd ever met. I thought that would have been the most insane thing I'd ever heard. But, in fact, that's what happened over the next 16 years," he said while delivering the keynote address at the 1992 Louisville Conference.

He fell in love with alcohol, and in time the alcohol owned him. "And it's a love affair. I mean, for me it was a love affair. When I started putting that stuff down my throat, everything changed. I became a good dancer. I became a more brilliant conversationalist. I became a better lover for my wife. I just became a better racing official. Where

I was clumsy in social situations, all of a sudden, I was really good in those situations; and it was just a magic thing," he said. "I don't think I've ever loved a woman as much as I loved what alcohol did for me. It transformed me, and it seemed to make me whole. The problem was that lasted about a year-and-a-half, and then everything started going down the drain. And what I did for the next over a dozen years was try and recapture that illusive feeling I got when I first started to drink."

Pete Drypolcher suffered all of the humiliations that go with the disease – the handcuffs, the jail cells, the hospital rooms, the realization that he was not being promoted because he was a drunk. "None of those things kept me from doing it. I thought, 'Tomorrow I'll do better, tomorrow I'll do better.' And the amazing thing is that I never really got fired. I just sort of got shunted aside, and I was one of those kind of people that thought, if I put up this facade that I'm a successful businessman, I'm a successful husband and a successful father, then I can't be an alcoholic. And my life was dedicated to putting up that facade. And because of that, I would sober up every third day, go to work at 4 and just work like a maniac till 9 at night; and then I would reward myself. And somehow the companies I worked for, even though they weren't real keen on that, they sort of tolerated my work and let me go along with that until 1976," he said. Then he quit putting up the facade and, in his words, lived to drink.

He also ended up in a hospital – for the 11th time – after an automobile accident south of Denver. "My clothes have been cut off of me. I've been stitched up, and I'm laying there nude with no earthly possessions," Drypolcher said. "My wife had by then left and gone to the Bahamas to live with her sister because she didn't want to see any more of my action." Then his doctor came in, and perhaps Drypolcher thought he would get some sympathy. Not so. "Pete, I'm not going to be your doctor any more," Drypolcher recalled him saying.

"He said, 'I've been practicing medicine for 32 years, and I have never seen a case as hopeless as yours. You're a hopeless alcoholic, and you're going to die very soon, and there's nothing I can do for you, and I don't want to see you die.' Then my wife called from the Bahamas when he was in the room, and he picked up the phone. And he said, 'Pat, your husband is a hopeless alcoholic and he's going to die, and you have your own life to live. I suggest that you file for divorce as soon as you get back to the States, and don't hurry back because he's never going to change.' " Then Drypolcher's boss at Centennial Race Track came to his room, and the doctor told him much the same thing: "Pete's a hopeless alcoholic. You need to fire him on the spot because he's going to die of this."

For the first time in his long career of drinking, someone had laid everything on the line for Pete Drypolcher. It was a classic intervention – and successful. "I haven't had a drink since that day," Drypolcher said. "I went into a twelve-step program, and it really worked for me."

Drypolcher said he often hears the complaint that life is not fair. "Well, I'm one of those people that wants to tell you that thank God life isn't fair, because if life were fair, I would be either in prison or dead. But because this doctor came in and told me the truth and because there were people who could reach out and tell me how to recover and give me a life-long program of recovery, then I feel like I'm the luckiest man alive," he said. The failed race-track employee became a highly successful executive within the Quarter Horse industry. He served as vice president and general manager of Santa Fe Racing, Inc., operator of The Downs at Santa Fe and The Downs at Albuquerque, before launching a consulting business within the racing industry. Over the years, he has helped many others to find sobriety.

"As managers and trainers and farm managers and track department heads and horsemen and jockey organizations, we must take time for these people. Don't fire or threaten them. Offer help," Drypolcher said. "Alcoholics, I think, when they do recover, they will really be grateful for the fact that you thought of them as a person and put their sobriety above everything else. And when they do come back to work for you, I think you'll have a great employee."

He offered an example of the satisfaction he has received from giving serious, meaningful help to an employee. A department head came in and "said, 'I have this friend who has the problem.' And it was so neat because I mean I knew exactly who had the problem, and it was so neat to be able to tell him what had happened to me,"

Drypolcher said. About six weeks later at 6 a.m., the supervisor called him and asked for help. Drypolcher made certain that he received it. A life was saved, and a race track gained a valuable, productive employee. And why not? Drypolcher read a brief section from the Big Book of Alcoholics Anonymous, and it is as true today as it was in 1939. It quotes a small-business owner: "There are two alcoholic employees who produce as much as five normal salesmen. But why not? They have a new attitude, and they have been saved from a living death."

Pete Drypolcher was saved from a living death and set on a path to recovery. In his turn, he has helped others onto that path. Like Pat Day, Pete Drypolcher is a winner.

Chapter 5

Silent No More

Jim Ryan once was a member of the silent majority. A successful home builder in Maryland, he entered Thoroughbred racing as a money-making avocation. He enjoyed the horses and the farm, to be sure, but he also considered them as another way of keeping score, a method of gauging how well he was doing in business, how well he was succeeding in life.

In truth, he was doing very well. By the early 1980s, his Ryehill Farm had bred and raced two high-quality colts, Quadratic and Smarten, and had collected two Eclipse Awards, for two-year-old filly champions Smart Angle and Heavenly Cause. The success of the operation was crowned in 1983 when Caveat, owned by Ryan and two partners, won the Belmont Stakes (G1).

With the classic victory, James P. Ryan had reached the top of the sport, and his place there was marked by his election to The Jockey Club. But, at roughly that time, Jim Ryan was undergoing a change in his life. He had endured a troubling divorce, retired from the business he had built – and had quit looking at Thoroughbred racing as a way of keeping score.

Ryan emerged from his midlife rite of passage with a new sense of religious faith, self-awareness, and self-esteem. He also was blessed with a new set of eyes, a new way of looking at the world. He looked at a Thoroughbred industry that had provided him with pleasure and profit, and he was saddened by what he saw. He saw the people of the backstretch, many of them impoverished and addicted, and he could be silent no more. No longer could he look at the horses and think of them only as an investment. "I really can't go to the winner's circle and just look at the brass nameplate or the horse and not see the individual. I was able to do that for years," Ryan said. "It's scary when you take your protection down, it really is. You feel vulnerable."

Ryan's wife at that time, Linda, sensitized him to the person holding the horse, the person who Ryan believes has been forgotten by the racing industry. "I really believe the horse is looked upon higher in this industry than the people that work with it," he said in 1989. "And I might even exaggerate and say that some of the dogs in the barns – the little pet dog with the nickname – is looked upon more sympathetically, if he died, versus somebody that's been an nonentity with no laces in their shoes, no socks, pus in his eyes, feeding a horse for the last seven years."

For several years now, Jim Ryan has spoken out eloquently and effectively on a topic that he considers to be Thoroughbred racing's Big Lie, the living conditions on America's race tracks. "It's a way of life," he said. "I never realized how powerful this subject is. You start dealing with the quality of life of an individual on the backstretch, you're not just dealing with his alcohol or drug addiction. You're dealing with the environment he came from, the environment she goes back to. Housing, the lack of recreation, the kitchen, the child that's locked in the room – it's so huge, they're afraid to open Pandora's box."

Jim Ryan also has, in the language common to the Western Pennsylvania hillsides from which he emerged, put his money where his mouth was. When he dispersed his 80 broodmares and weanlings in November, 1988, he took more than $1-million and put it into substance-abuse programs on North America's race tracks. He largely financed the first Conference on Alcohol and Drug Abuse Programs for the Horse Racing Industry, held in Louisville in 1989, and he subsequently provided substantial assistance to in-patient care and the Race Track Chaplaincy of America. And those were only a few of the more public examples of the Ryan Family Foundation's giving. He also has pressed Maryland's race tracks to build substance-free dormitories.

Ryan knew that he could not give all of his wealth away – after all, he believed that his children deserved to share in some of the fruits of his labors – but he was doing his very best to share a substantial portion of his wealth. "We wanted to help. We wanted to leave something on the table from the dispersal," Ryan said of the decision to put up $20,000 matching grants for 54 race-track programs. "I never had an idea of how much it was needed." A measure of Ryan's success was that, five years after the first grants, all of the programs at existing tracks were still in operation. (Some programs dissolved when the tracks they served went out of business.)

The Ryan Family Foundation grant was to be matched by the race track. "With $40,000, you can fund the administrative salary of a counselor. That's how we came up with the $20,000. Matching funds are a good way to get local involvement," Ryan said. The effort has paid off in other ways for Ryan. "I have never gotten as much out of the racing industry as I have this year. I have a piece of what we've done," he said in 1989. "Giving is very lasting."

Ryan provided more than money to the effort. He provided business guidance and, more importantly, inspiration. "He is a person who can make a change. He is a person who will stand up," said Bob Babes, who established the backstretch counseling programs at the Maryland tracks, at the 1989 Louisville Conference. Like anyone who speaks out, Jim Ryan has paid a price.

He has, in some quarters, been called a fool. Friends have told him that he was wasting his wealth, giving it to assist people who do not appreciate the help. Effectively, he was told: "You're going to waste your money, Jim. You're pouring money down a sewer." Ryan dismisses that as "blaming the victim" and another aspect of the Big Lie on the race track. "What I'm talking about is kind of heresy. There are a lot of people very angry that we're here," he said in his keynote address to the 1989 Louisville Conference. "They say, 'Listen, you hurt this industry and they won't have a job. You put any doubts in the bettors' minds that the horse might not function well because of an addiction of a handler — that would devastate the betting handle, provide less money to the industry. And who are you helping, Jim?' I think the best thing that we can do is be honest and direct. Don't play God here. It's bad. The industry has elected to spend, I believe, $7.4-million for testing of horses for drugs, and their reasoning is to ensure the betting public they're getting a fair deal. They're spending zero on the people that take care of the horses."

Ryan also is no longer a member of The Jockey Club. With considerable personal pain, he resigned in August, 1989, as a matter of conscience after his advocacy resulted in his removal from the committee overseeing the Jockey Club Foundation. "I felt very alone," he said. Indeed he was. No one spoke up for him at The Jockey Club's membership meeting, and very few approached him after the meeting to express their support privately.

At that time, Jim Ryan was living comfortably on 150 acres of Ryehill Farm in Mt. Airy, Maryland, at the edge of the ever-growing Washington-Baltimore metropolis. Originally, the farm had 300 acres, but the other half has been subdivided into three-acre building lots. In his business career, Jim Ryan had earned a fortune, and he made provision for his children to have a legacy. But — carefully, thoughtfully, compassionately — he was giving away his wealth.

His benevolence is based on a deep and abiding religious faith that has developed over many years. He was only following the biblical imperative to provide for others, said Ryan, who summarized his own philosophy: "There's enough here for everybody. We've got to do more sharing."

In his 1989 keynote address, Ryan shared much of himself before counselors, chaplains, and other race-track industry members at the five-day Louisville session. Ryan obtained a master's degree in pastoral counseling at Baltimore's Loyola College, and — to provide counseling and therapy to others — he too made the passage back through time, back to the roots of his life. Now, he could speak with understanding about his father, who died in 1941, when Jim Ryan was 8-years-old. His father broke out of the mold, by hard work gaining a better life for his family in Pittsburgh. But he also was a violent alcoholic who abused his wife physically and his son Jim psychologically. As a youngster, Jim Ryan wanted desperately to be his father's son, to be at the Old Man's side when he went off on a job. All he received was rejection. "I felt one feeling in my first eight years from my father, and that was one of rejection. I had blond hair and he was dark-haired — I was my mother's son. I have a younger brother who was my dad's favorite — he had dark hair," he said.

Like others who have tasted the bitterness of their father's rejection, Jim Ryan grew up with a blast furnace inside him, with a burning desire to succeed. "I wanted to be good at everything. I remember when I played football (at Mount Lebanon High School), they'd have sweatshirts out, I'd run to the sweatshirts and always pick out the number one, and I always wore that. And I heard that the quarterback was the head of the team, so I wanted to be quarterback. Unfortunately, I didn't grow very much, and ended up being quarterback on a losing team, and we didn't do that well," he said. "But it was my posture – it was my program. I had such a low self-worth that I would do everything to try to achieve, to accomplish it. And I did that, really, for 40-some years. "

He accomplished a lot in those 40-odd years. He was only the second member of his family to graduate from college, "and the first was a nun," he said. He became a jet-fighter pilot although he secretly was frightened of the planes and the speed. With his oldest brother, Edward, he helped to develop Ryan Homes, which was the Pittsburgh area's leading home builder in the 1950s and 1960s. He said, though, that he and his brother were "always arm-wrestling figuratively, trying to be the family hero." As a result, Jim Ryan left the company and Pittsburgh in the mid-1960s. In 1967, he founded Ryland Homes, which was one of the builders of the highly successful Columbia planned community. By the time Jim Ryan retired from the board, Ryland Homes had built more than 100,000 houses.

His father's addiction was to alcohol, and Jim Ryan's addiction was to work. The company, now publicly owned, prospered, and so did Ryan. He and his former wife, Eleanor, bought the Mt. Airy farm in 1970 and transformed the former cattle operation into one of the bright lights of Maryland breeding. But, at the height of his success, all was not well with Jim Ryan. In part because of his Roman Catholic heritage, he was deeply troubled by the break-up of a 28-year marriage.

Through his relationship with Linda in those years and through his exploration to his roots, he achieved peace with his father and with himself. "I spent all those years chasing my father. In the last two years, I've started thinking of my parents together. I'm pulling together my two poles," he said in 1989. "Healing never took place until I went back with Christ's presence and forgave my dad. It took me a long time before this has ever happened."

He also permits himself to feel. When he resigned from Ryland's board of directors in 1986, "I bawled for about 12 minutes," he said.

Linda Ryan introduced Jim Ryan to the caring professions. He met her almost by chance, at a time when he was struggling with the divorce and his concerns about his worth as an individual. Jim Ryan was troubled by the fear that he had turned into a tough son of a bitch – just like his dad. "The big fear was that I thought I was not a good candidate for a meaningful relationship." But then Jim met Linda. "She ran a center for 54 retarded adults called Carroll Center, and they had a Christmas party," he said. "Well, I'd never been to a dinner there. Well, I saw this woman – I saw Linda, going around with her Kleenex, wiping the spaghetti off some of her clients' lips. And I watched her – I really studied her. And I said to myself, without knowing it: 'If she can love these, she could love me.' " About two years later, they were married.

She also helped him to see clearly the living conditions at the track, to see the person holding the shank as well as the horse at the end of it. "I didn't know what the term 'caring profession' meant," he said. "I was so focused on building houses, I had blinkers on. I read, I knew as much as I could about homebuilding. But this idea of a caring profession was intriguing to me, and it introduced me to a world that, thank God, I've had a chance to be exposed to." He has attempted to remove the blinkers from others within the industry, and not with great success. The racing industry often supports the poor living and working conditions with its silence, he contended.

The conditions indeed can be stark: People living in tack rooms, in rooms smaller than jail cells, out of their cars, working for wages that sometimes do not reach the legal minimum. They are people living in an environment where alcohol is a way of life and a part of the reward system. How often does the barn get a case of beer when the big horse wins a race? Certainly, drugs do not stop at the stable gate, no matter how efficient the security system is. "People are dying constantly," he said. "I had a chaplain say that we sprinkled the ashes of 22 alcoholics on this track – there's a plaque that shows it. That's sick. A plaque. When are you going to stand up and be heard? When are we? There's a piece of us that has voted with the system, with our silence, with our compliance to management."

All of this silence and compliance, Ryan said, adds up to bad business – for the employers, for the race tracks, for the bettors, and for the entire industry. "It's bad business to run your business with people who are addicted," he said. "Statistics have shown that 18 percent of addicted persons will steal from their employer."

Those are strong words, indeed, and Jim Ryan used them frequently with people who did not want to hear those words. They cost him his membership on The Jockey Club, but he said he holds no anger over the incident. "I don't want to judge all of the people involved. They are caring people who are insulated. They can't handle someone with bad breath and pus in their eyes saying they need help," Ryan said.

The issue concerned the earnings from the Jockey Club Foundation, whose capital totaled approximately $7-million in 1989. Ryan wanted the foundation to put its healthy investment income – about $1-million annually, representing a 15 percent return – into drug and alcohol programs. He was told that the foundation would continue to give away 6.5 percent annually in assistance to individuals. The remainder would be retained for "a rainy day," he was told. If he would have been thinking of a rejoinder to that statement, Ryan said, he would have urged Jockey Club members to open the windows. "I would have said: 'Get out of your Trustees Room, get out of your office on Park Avenue, and go back to the backstretch. It's pouring back there.' It is pouring back there. I had no idea it was this bad when we started."

Ryan had advocated spending 10 percent of the Jockey Club Foundation's money – less than the full amount of the interest income annually – on substance-abuse programs. The response was to remove Ryan from the foundation's committee, and then to misrepresent the circumstances: the foundation's chairman told Jockey Club members that he had resigned from the committee. When Ogden Mills Phipps, Jockey Club chairman, took the lectern after the erroneous statement, Ryan demanded a correction. "And he says: 'Unfortunately, my job is tough sometimes, and I had to remove Jim Ryan from the foundation committee.' I said: 'Would you tell them why, Dinny?' And he said: 'Well, the meetings were very acrimonious.' If I had only known what that meant, I could have responded to it. We had differences of opinion. I got up and I said: 'First of all, I want to thank Dinny for correcting that I didn't resign. I wanted to stay on, I wanted to give this money away because there's a real need out there.' And I said it to all the general membership," Ryan said. "And I said, 'There's a need back there. And I wish I knew you better to talk about it, but I think I'm going to leave The Jockey Club.' Then I hesitated and I said: 'No, I know I'm going to leave.' In my business, when we had differences of opinion, we loved it. We loved it. If you all agree, you have too many people in the room. You want differences of opinion. You don't box the truth, you only approach it. And the only way you can look at it is multi-dimensional. I was a dissident; I did have a different opinion. But I loved it. And I said: 'Here the reaction is to remove me from the committee. I don't want to be a part of this.' " Ryan departed in sadness, but he also felt he should leave with a positive message, rather than allowing bitterness and negativism to overtake his thinking.

Jim Ryan's desire to spend the Jockey Club Foundation's money grew out of some hard-headed business sense and a lesson from his mother. He chided the counselors at the 1989 Louisville Conference for not standing up for themselves and demanding higher salaries. In business, Ryland had given out bonuses and trips to generate greater productivity and thus higher profits. And, money spent on drug and alcohol therapy can be highly beneficial. "It's a reality. Treatment can return a productive person to life," Ryan said.

Just as in business, Ryan wants money to be used efficiently, although health care and social services cannot be equated with buying two-by-fours. Not all of the money will turn around lives, but some of it will, he said. Here, a lesson learned from Mary Ryan applies. During World War II, Ed Ryan was shot down over Austria and confined in a prisoner-of-war camp. His mother would send packages to him through the Red Cross, and not all of the contents would arrive safely. But she was not discouraged. "She'd say, 'I don't care as long as something gets there.' And she'd begin to prepare another package," Ryan said.

For the race tracks' drug and alcohol programs, the question is where the next package will come from. He worried about 1990 and beyond, but race tracks and some horsemen's associations have decided that it is good business to invest in the health of their employees. Ryan also suggested that the counseling programs lobby in their states to get funds from uncashed tickets for backstretch programs. "What use can be better than putting it to work right on the track?" he asked. "It's a negotiable, arm-wrestling situation for you. We must lobby toward that end. It's the best shot I know."

He also suggested that the counselors look to companies in their regions and to people within the industry. "Different people are coming up and saying, 'Where can I fund?' There's a lot of money in this industry, and there's a lot of good people that have it. Don't get it in your mind that someone with money isn't sensitive, isn't as caring as you are. They're insulated. They're insulated with their limousines and with their air conditioning and with their good dental care and their nice smile. But they're very caring," he said. "I know if there was an accident in the limousine, and somebody lost an arm, the people would take whatever they have on to bind it, would go to the hospital, do whatever they had to. I was one of them for 40 years." But then he started looking at the person taking care of his horses and others' horses – the human being at the end of the shank – and he could no longer be silent. "The quality of life on the backstretch is horrendous. Don't let it exist without making some noise," he told the Louisville Conference in 1989. Jim Ryan certainly made certain that his voice was heard – clearly, compellingly, and constructively. He could be silent no more. Jim and Linda Ryan were divorced in the mid-1990s, and Jim Ryan remarried and was living in East Jerusalem, Israel, in 1997. He indeed was far from the race track most of the time, but – a decade after his dispersal – his influence lived on in the race-track programs that were begun with his money and, as importantly, his inspiration.

Chapter 6

A Standard of Excellence

Firstst question: Would you hire this individual as your company's chief executive officer?

The candidate goes before the board of his current company and tells the directors he has identified a problem that is costing the company tens of thousands of dollars each year and seriously denting the bottom line – the company's profits. The problem also is hurting the corporation's competitiveness, and it is endangering the company's reputation within its community and the corporate world. And, after quantifying the problem for the directors, your CEO candidate says that he is going to do nothing about the problem, that he feels incapable of doing anything about the problem, and that he is going to ignore the problem until someone else comes along to fix it.

Second question: Why would you consider this guy in the first place?

Third question: How long is this CEO going to be gainfully employed?

The answer to the third question is that his attitude, if verbalized, would most likely put him on the street in a matter of minutes. The directors would waste little time getting rid of him, and they would not bother with such niceties as a gold watch. But most chief executive officers do not say that they are sitting on a time bomb – known as substance abuse – and plan to do nothing about it. They simply ignore the problem. "That's what many CEOs have said in the business place today," Rodney Wolford, then chief executive officer of Louisville's Alliant Health System, said at the 1989 Conference on Alcohol and Drug Abuse Programs for the Horse Racing Industry. Alliant, whose Norton Psychiatric Clinic was a sponsor of the first five

Louisville conferences, chose not to remain silent about the problem. A few days before the first Louisville Conference, Alliant had announced its program to eliminate substance abuse within its work force. The standard that it set – the only standard that it thought was acceptable or defensible – was zero tolerance for drugs and alcohol in the work place.

"Although Alliant is a tax-exempt organization, it is a large business. We have 4,200 employees. Some have drug and alcohol addictions, and I'm concerned about what that does to us, for our quality and our future success," he said. "But most importantly, I'm concerned what drugs and alcohol are doing to all of America's business. In a highly competitive world – and we are in a world market now, in a highly competitive world market – it's easy to conclude that drugs and alcohol in the work place can't help us. In fact, I think that the harm that drugs and alcohol do to us in the work place right now hurts us far more than we can ever imagine, in our competitive position in the world."

The problems, as presented by Wolford, present some very disturbing statistics. "Slightly over 10 percent of Americans – staggering number, 18 million adults, 4.6 million adolescents – have a drug and alcohol dependency. The total economic cost – now, this is according to the National Association of State Alcohol and Drug Abuse Directors – through the loss of productivity, absenteeism, and errors, was estimated in 1984 to be $176-billion in our country. Now that takes a pretty good chunk of our GNP (gross national product, and also identified as GDP, gross domestic product) in terms of wasted effort, because of drug and alcohol addiction in the work place," said Wolford, who estimated the 1989 cost at above $200-billion. "I can tell you that the problem has not got any less since then. The annual cost of treatment – and this shows you where our priorities are – was $3 billion in 1987. That gives you a real good feeling that, while we recognize that it's costing us $200 billion-plus, we're only spending $3 billion. Now, those numbers are far beyond my comprehension, as to the total magnitude. But in a country our size, $200 billion makes a big difference in the world economy that we're competing in.

"Federal experts estimated that 10 percent to 23 percent of the workers have used dangerous drugs on the job. According to the survey by the Cocaine National Hotline, 75 percent of drug users admitted to using drugs on the job; 44 percent sold to fellow co-workers; 18 percent had job-related accidents attributable to using drugs on the job; and 18 percent had stolen from employers to help support their addiction. These are addicts calling into the national hotline, giving this survey and giving these numbers to these individuals. So I think it's valid that we can say, we've got a problem in the work place. Another report out of Nation's Business gives the characteristics of drug users: That they're late 3 1/2 times as much; 2 1/2 times as many absences; 5 times more likely to file a workers's comp claim; and they're involved in accidents 3.5 times more than the non-addicted worker," Wolford said.

"In my own industry, it gets very scary. Because you say, you're in the health-care industry, you shouldn't have these problems because we entrust ourselves to you. But believe me, we got the problem. We're supposed to be here to help people. People put their lives in our hands every day. But health-care workers have the same problems as everyone else. In fact, they may be more vulnerable, when you look at it. Health-care workers have high stress, they have high availability of drugs, and this contributes to that vulnerability. The statistics for health care seem to demonstrate this. There's never any good statistics on physicians, because they do a wonderful job of hiding their problems within their profession. But it is estimated – and I think this estimate is very close – that there is at least 15 percent that have addiction problems in medicine. Eight to 10 percent of the nurses are alcoholics. One out of three disciplinary cases that nurses have are drug-related. And finally, you get to the executives and the managers, covering all industries. Fully 10 percent have drug and alcohol addictions, and that shouldn't surprise any one of us, because addiction knows no boundaries, as we look across all industries."

How has this continued? As was stated before, why has American business not risen up and attacked this problem whose cost is more than equal to our nation's deficit spending each year? A campaign against substance abuse and addiction would be a creative way to attack the national debt, but a national campaign of this sort – as contrasted with a national war on drugs or crime – has not been mounted. Why? Wolford had an answer that did not spare most of his fellow corporate executives.

"American business has a problem. And quite honestly, I don't think they've addressed that problem. You and I, as business people, all share that problem. Have we done anything about it? No, I don't think we have. But I'm satisfied and determined, speaking as a business person, that we can do something about it," he said. "I believe that toleration and complacency in the business place has worked positively toward our problem. And when I say positively – it's built the problem. Somehow or another, I believe, business could work against that problem and cause it to be less. We have contributed, in terms of what we do in our business place, to our national drug and alcohol addiction problems. In the face of these statistics – the cost, the errors, the loss of profits – business leaders are presented with multiple options. They can choose to ignore the problem, like many others have done before them. Pass the buck to someone else and say: 'No, it's your problem, government. Do something for me.' Or: 'It's your problem, family. Take care of it for me. Don't send me those employees who have addiction problems.' Or they could decide that the buck stops at their office, at their desk."

Wolford noted that addiction in the work place is much like a stone thrown into a pond. The effects – the ripples from the stone – radiate outward from the point of impact. "Mental stress to other employees – we don't count that in the statistics," he said. "If you've got an addicted employee and they come to work constantly and they have less productivity and they're causing problems with behavioral problems on the work site, do you know how demoralizing that is to the fellow employees around it and the productivity that that reduces in your organization?"

The effects of addiction can touch the entire work place, and several participants in the Louisville Conference have touched on the issue of the toxic work place. Dr. Bill Jacyk of Winnipeg, Manitoba – a public-health physician who attended the 1991 Louisville Conference – said he was struck by "the difficulty still in understanding this as a disease that not only affects the people who are chemically dependent but those who are working around somebody who's chemically dependent. What you have and what I've heard people describe basically are toxic work places. If you look at health-care costs – and these come from your country – health-care costs of people who are related to people who are chemically dependent are just as high as the individual who is chemically dependent. So there's a stress-related illness here that is not being totally exposed although we're looking at the tip of the iceberg. And I'd really like to see something that would begin to look at your work places as either being healthy work places or toxic work places, and I don't think there's anything in between," he said.

Are North America's race-track backstretches toxic work places? If Dr. Jacyk's definition is accepted – that work places are either healthy or toxic – then the stable areas are most definitely toxic. Lori Weinegar said she and Philadelphia Park's chaplain, the Rev. Nicholas Salios, had had discussions about "doing good work in a bad place." Toxic work places or bad places, they certainly are far removed from the idyllic, fairy-tale vision of the race track backstretch where happy workers tended to horses out of their love for the animals and the racing sport. But John Cashman, a Standardbred horseman who served as the American Horse Council's chairman and delivered the Louisville Conference's 1991 keynote address, said the romantic imagery has persisted despite the reality. "Our industry has been slow to recognize these facts and to establish the sort of environment that will react to those facts. Some have taken a fatalistic view that alcohol and drugs have always been part of the race track environment and that they always will be there. It's not at all hard to hear stories about race track characters who feature a hard-drinking lifestyle, but when sober, are the best in the business," he said. "Those who see romance or joy in addiction for sure have not been there. Those who see romance or joy in addiction for sure have not had to run a business that depended on such addicted individuals."

For all the individuals who work at North America's race tracks and for the horse-racing industry, Cashman strongly urged that a new standard be adopted: zero tolerance for impairment. "The race track is no place for drugs. The race track is no place for those who use illegal drugs or use legal drugs illegally. It is no place for individuals who have become impaired by alcohol that they used legally but unwisely to excess. The race track is no place for the addicted person, whether that person is addicted to alcohol or to other drugs," he said. "In short, the race track is first and foremost a work place for those in the industry. Impairment in the work place, whether from alcohol or from other drugs, can't be tolerated. That statement is as true for impairment in the board room or horse farm as it is for impairment in the tack room. There is no place on the race track where impairment is a good idea or where there is good reason to tolerate impairment due to alcohol or other drugs."

Cashman said every company must realize that the problems of a broader society – problems such as alcohol and drug addiction – will invade the work place if the addictions are not addressed aggressively. For the racing industry, both the reality and the image are vitally important. "Our industry in the public eye has been tainted by the image of a sleazy fellow who is supposed to have the inside information on which horse will win and why," he said. "The very fact that we drug test the winning horse tells us what image we have been trying to counter. The same image problem applies to our personnel. In the community, they are our image. What they do reflects on us. If they are detrimental to the community when off the track, then our negative image is reinforced. If they are solid citizens, our positive image is reinforced. Who can measure the good when, around Kentucky Derby time, jockeys converge on children's hospitals and visit sick kids? Who can measure the harm done when an industry leader is charged with using cocaine while his business practices are under investigation? Those images, whether negative or positive, translate directly into a healthy or unhealthy business status at the race track.

"For example, the very best way to attract new patrons to the racing industry is through group and corporate sales. When the race track can relate to other major community corporations at the same level, those corporations will treat their employees to a day at the races. Those employees will come back in some numbers as new patrons of the race track. Community corporations will not come to the race track if it has a bad image or if the industry has a bad image, and neither will their employees. Without new patrons, the racing industry will suffer."

At a time of crisis, Cashman said, the racing industry must consider its productivity – whether it is getting the greatest value from the people it employs. "Every race track today faces stiff competition from other entertainment opportunities. Like any other business, we are having to do more with less. That means assuring that every employee, whether at the pari-mutuel window or grooming a horse or helping cut down the time between races, must be fully productive. No industry today can survive with an impaired work force," he said. "If we know that we have addicted workers and workers who are abusing alcohol or drugs to solve problems, then we have to change that. It's not a matter of choice or humanitarian interest. It's just good business."

As a policy of good business, many American corporations have implemented substance-abuse policies within the work place. They have, in general, combined a firm stance on not hiring those with impairments to a firm but compassionate helping hand for existing employees who have or have developed addictions. In the clearest terms, though, these companies have enunciated a policy that echoes a statement by Rear Admiral Paul J. Mulloy, U.S. Navy retired: "Not on my ship, not in my Navy." In his final active-duty assignment, Admiral Mulloy put into effect the Navy's program for attacking substance abuse in the service — a strategy that cut substance abuse from 48 percent in 1982 to less than 2 percent a decade later. Was it an expensive program? You bet. But the Navy calculated that it got back $12 for every dollar that it spent. For other companies, the payback rate has been 9-to-1 or higher.

Alliant's Wolford said the most important element of any program is confrontation — the business must confront that it has a problem, and the business must in turn confront those who have a substance-abuse problem. "If a business takes a strong stand of saying: 'We will not tolerate drug and alcohol addiction in the work place,' the employed, addicted person is suddenly confronted. They're confronted with a strong crisis in their life. It's something we must do. It is my understanding that we must do that with an addicted person, to get them to realize the situation that they're in. They understand, at that point in time, that he or she may lose their job. They may not be able to support their family, if they lose their job, and they may not be able to easily get another job. They do have a job, and they feel that if they can correct the problem, they will probably keep that job. That's what we've got to tell them. Is this bad for the individual? I'm not sure it is. Because I think that we need to confront those individuals with that problem," he said. "It may be this confrontation, this feeling of the world closing in on that employee, that finally causes him to reach bottom and turn around and seek help, and return as a first-class employee. That is where we help the individual. By simply saying, we recognize your problem, we're going to confront you with that problem, and you must seek help if we confront you with that problem. Otherwise, you will not be employed with us, because we cannot afford to maintain you if you are not a productive employee, and an addicted employee."

Alliant's program contained four elements: Prevention, education, discovery, and rehabilitation. Prevention involved testing every job applicant, for a cleaning position or for chief executive officers, and requiring a clean test. "In Portland, Oregon, where I implemented this policy in 1985, this policy in the early months rejected 20 percent of the successful applicants," Wolford said. "Soon thereafter, we gained the reputation of saying: 'We will not accept those who have an addiction problem or those who have drugs that test positively in their bloodstream.' That percentage fell very drastically after that point in time. In other words, our reputation went out into the community, that we're asking for zero tolerance in our organization."

The policy had similar effects in Louisville. A year later, Gaylia Bond, employee relations manager at Alliant, reported that of 1,027 otherwise successful job applicants, 24 had been rejected because of a positive test. "An analysis of results on the applicant side is that we believe our program is discouraging abusers from even applying for employment with us, but there have also been many others who failed to show up for that test," she said. "They've gone through this employment process. They're right down to the wire on being hired, and they have to call and make an appointment for that drug test, and then they never show. Well, we don't know for sure, but we suspect why they don't show."

Education, the second element of Alliant's zero-tolerance policy, has many facets. Education included teaching employees — or, in the Navy's example, seamen and officers — to recognize addictions and where to seek help. "We're not going to win this until we win the hearts and minds of the worker," Admiral Mulloy said at the 1990 Louisville Conference. "Training and education cannot be stressed enough. How do you get rid of vincible ignorance if you don't teach what is the problem? What are the substances? How many times have we been confronted with non-recognition of somebody that's got a problem? How are you going to help them if you don't know what it looks like or what it's about?"

If the individual recognizes a problem, the system must offer them immunity to seek help. Admitting an addiction or dependency must lead to help rather than to a pink slip or a general discharge. "If anybody seeks help, we must provide them with immunity or you'll never solve that problem. Allow them a way to get help," Admiral Mulloy said. "Let's get rid of the abuse, not the abuser. Then you'll win. Don't drive it underground. But if they keep fiddling with you, have that hammer ready."

Often, the communication involves not only the worker but also the worker's representative – whether it is a union or a horsemen's organization. Dr. Frank Kuzmits of the University of Louisville's School of Business and Public Administration said Oldsmobile was successful in implementing a substance-abuse program because it enlisted the United Auto Workers as its partner in the effort.

In addition, managers and supervisors are taught how to recognize a problem and how to confront the employee. Oldsmobile trained their supervisors, assembly-line workers, and plant managers to identify troubled employees through the ways they behave. "The way they're going to behave differently will boil down to attendance and absenteeism problems, interpersonal relationships, and productivity, whether that's accidents or injuries," Kuzmits said. "Supervisory training was a very key ingredient in the whole thing from a general and industrial approach, to make sure that people go through rigorous training on how to deal with their problems."

Within the horse racing industry, Kuzmits said, supervision basically comes down to the trainer or, in a large operation, an assistant trainer or foreman. "You can't have a successful rehabilitation program if you don't have somebody who is observing performance and getting that person to undergo treatment. If you've got a trainer or an owner or somebody that's looking the other way, it's not going to

work. That's why I think the trainers are key people in this whole thing," he said. "The worst thing you can do with a troubled employee – or what you feel is a potentially troubled employee – is ignore it, because it's not going to go away. It's just going to get worse.
Another very bad thing to do, of course, is try to get rid of that employee by transferring him or her to another unit or somehow getting rid of that employee – forcing the employee to quit. It's not going to work."

The next logical step, in both the Alliant system and other employee-assistance programs, is to identify and quantify the problem as a method of forcing the employee to confront his or her addiction. In most cases, this step involves testing, and corporations have approached this step thoughtfully and carefully. Companies that have done testing well have communicated with their employees in advance of the program's initiation and have effectively gained the employees' assent to such a program. Admiral Mulloy suggested that focus groups within corporations have been used successfully to achieve a consensus. The reason for the small-group meetings on a specific topic "is to get optimum employee involvement in formulating your policy. Take your time. The average corporation I've been talking with takes anywhere from 12-to-15 months just to get a program on line. I totally agree with that. General Dynamics took two years. Then they took a year to put it in effect. Texas Instruments took over a year and a half of developing through focus groups a consensus about their policy, and in January (1990) they instituted full random or what they call universal testing because all the employees asked for it. It tells you what's happening," he said.

Both Wolford and Admiral Mulloy noted that court decisions generally have backed up the rights of businesses to conduct testing – if it is done properly. Mulloy said the testing must be done forensically – effectively, beyond a shadow of a doubt. "You got to do it right, or you don't do it at all. And if there's any doubt, not the lawyers' reasonable doubt, throw it out. That should be in your policy, meaning throw it out in favor of the individual; and you'll win. Instead of driving things underground, you're always keeping it up with people wanting to be on your side," he said.

Alliant's policy of testing was based on probable cause, and not just on one supervisor's observations or suspicions. "The decision to test under our policy for probable cause must consider two things: some behavior that is different. Something's changed in the way this employee is behaving at work," Bond said. "It could be absenteeism, performance, mood, whatever. It must be something there that's going on that can be observed. It might be even the typical physical signs as well. And in addition to that, there has to be some reason to suspect that this behavior is linked to drug and alcohol use. Whenever a supervisor has suspicion, the supervisor gives me a call; and we discuss both of these things: What behavior are you observing, and what reason do you believe that this is linked to drug or alcohol? Then we decide whether the test is a go or no-go. At that time the supervisor, along with a second management person, if possible, confronts the employee and again asks for explanations. We're always trying to understand what is going on. And depending on what the employee then discusses with the supervisor, again the decision is made whether to test or not test. If the decision is to go, the employee is escorted to our employee health service; and at our health service, a body-fluid collection is made by a registered nurse. The sample is sent to a reference lab, and we also use the chain-of-custody protocol. We do everything possible to protect the employee's right of privacy. We also use confirmation testing, and we test for alcohol, marijuana, opiates, and cocaine. So far the results that have come back positive have all been marijuana, I think – maybe one cocaine," she said in 1990 of the five positive tests in the previous year.

"The policy is not meant to be punitive but to have a very strong push toward rehabilitation. The employee is suspended pending the outcome of the test; and on the first occurrence of a positive test, the employee receives a mandatory referral to our employee-assistance program. The employee has seven days to set up the appointment. He must follow and complete the counselor's recommendations, and the employee must report back to the supervisor about his progress. If the employee does not fulfill one of these requirements, he or she is terminated. On a second occurrence of a positive test, the employee is terminated. Everybody gets one free shot, and we want that person to be rehabilitated. We also believe that it's costly to fire people, and we try to avoid that; and we feel like that we're doing everything we can to push the employee toward rehab. But the bottom line, it's the employee's choice; and we cannot risk, if it occurs a second time, we cannot risk having an employee impaired in a health-care work place. It is just too risky," she said.

Bond also noted that employees can be disciplined and terminated for illegal drug activities away from the work place. "Now this is something that may be a little out of the ordinary, but we think it's also important. If an employee of ours is arrested and convicted of trafficking off site, it's automatic termination. We cannot afford to have someone trafficking anywhere as an employee in one of our hospitals. Again, it's very important that we have both the disciplinary-part and the rehabilitation-part components of the policy. We want to help. We want to provide the support and the encouragement and the expert counseling, but we also want the employee to accept the responsibilities and the consequences of his or her own behavior; and that is the decision to be impaired at work or to engage in off-site, illegal activity."

Wolford, in his 1989 presentation, emphasized that the policy must apply to everyone and that no one should be permitted to slip through as a result of conscious or unconscious enabling. "And possibly the biggest hazard is exercising the double standard, which we're all capable of doing. If you let ol' Bill continue, because ol' Bill has been drunk for 15 years and nobody is going to do anything about him simply because he has been that way for a long time and you simply don't want to do anything about it, you're exercising a double standard," Wolford said. "If you let your own addiction continue, or one of your executives, you've exercised a double standard. And your failure to act will condone the situation and quite honestly will devastate the morale of the organization, like any other policy that you implement but choose not to follow."

Admiral Mulloy said that, after discovery and rehabilitation, the Navy took the next logical step, which is to enrich the environment so that boredom and inactivity are reduced. "When you crack down on drugs and booze, you better give them an alternative. In the service, what we developed was one of the finest fitness programs we've ever had; and we should have done this a long time ago. Who should be more fit than the folks that are defending this great country of ours? So we put that in. Well, the kids today are very high on being squared away, feeling good about themselves. Capitalize on that. These are your future employees. These are the ones you want to be promoted into leadership positions. Make it available. We opened up all-night movies, gyms. Maybe a corporation should look at things like having an open ticket for all people working in the company in one of these health spas. There are companies, for example, that are offering incentives that if a person stays within their body weight, fat content, they give them cash incentives at the end of the year," he said. "Now this is good cost-incentive stuff. But the main thing is you get people high on themselves. Get the families involved, picnics, good things to do in life. There are a lot of wonderful things to do in life besides getting blown away."

Kuzmits also emphasized that rehabilitation pays off handsomely, and he cited the experience of Oldsmobile. Employees who completed rehabilitation programs had "significant reductions in absenteeism, grievances, disciplinary actions, accidents, and lost wages. They estimated that an annual $57,000 cost of the program returned $234,000 in the first year only, economic benefits due to reductions in health care, and improvements in productivity," he said. Although not every employee will successfully complete rehabilitation, "the estimated success rate for most industry EAPs is somewhere in between 65 and 85 percent, depending on the quality of the program and how well it's administered, how soon you catch a troubled employee, and get him or her into treatment," Kuzmits said. The way to get top management behind the rehabilitation programs is to emphasize dollars-and-cents arguments. "If you want to talk about the ethical and morality issues, fine. I'm not sure that that's going to wake everybody up. But when you start talking dollars and cents, they start to listen. So I guess, you know, my message is, it's profitable. It's very simple. It's going to help the bottom line," he said. "And race track owners and managers and farm owners and managers and trainers have got to listen to that message because we're talking about profits."

Chapter 7

In the Shedrow and on the Farm

Through the years, Carl A. Nafzger has worn many hats. In his 20s, he was one of the world's best rodeo bull riders, ranking third in 1963. In the early days of ABC's Wide World of Sports, Jim McKay — wearing an incongruous ten-gallon hat — interviewed a lanky, 21-year-old cowboy from Texas who had just won a Las Vegas Rodeo event. It was Carl Nafzger. With his wife and partner, Wanda, Nafzger started out with two Thoroughbreds, representing their savings and some family investment. He worked as a farrier and an exercise rider, but he never took his eye off the goal, to reach the top of the sport. He aimed for the sky, and he achieved his ambition through hard work, intelligence, and a natural affinity for horses. Nafzger has been a successful trainer for many years, and he picked up his "comma" in 1990. His comma? Yes, Nafzger said, his comma, as in Carl Nafzger (comma) trainer of 1990 Kentucky Derby winner Unbridled. The comma is very important. It allows the trainer to answer honestly and without reservation the question that is asked nearly every time he encounters a stranger who knows little about Thoroughbred racing. The question, of course, is: "Have you ever trained a Kentucky Derby winner?" Nafzger also trained Unbridled to a victory in the 1990 $3-million Breeders' Cup Classic, but he perhaps will always be best remembered for his poignant Derby race call for Mrs. Frances Genter, Unbridled's 92-year-old owner, as her blaze-faced wonder pounded through Churchill Downs's stretch: "He's taking the lead! Mrs. Genter, you're going to win the Kentucky Derby!" Then, as Unbridled neared the wire, he said: "There he is, there is," to focus her attention on the finish line, where Unbridled would pass 3 1/2 lengths ahead of Summer Squall. "You've won the Kentucky

Derby, Mrs. Genter. I love you." That was unrehearsed, unpremeditated. That was the real stuff, the real Carl Nafzger. And he did not even know that the ABC microphone on his lapel was operating throughout the race.

In 1994, Nafzger added another hat: author. For years, even before Unbridled's Derby victory, he had wanted to write a book about training horses. Nafzger always has thought thoroughly and deeply about horses and the horse business, and he distilled a significant portion of his thoughts and wisdom into *Traits of a Winner: The Formula for Developing Thoroughbred Race Horses.*[1] In the book and in the daily training regimen, the Nafzgers are true to the dictum that Nafzger was taught 40 years ago by a high school mathematics teacher in Texas. "He told us we should be the best that we can be. If you're going to be a bum, be the best bum that you can be," Nafzger said. "When we got into racing, we wanted to be the best that we can be."

The Nafzgers' approach to being the best that they can be has, at base, two parts. First, get to know the horse and adapt the training regimen to make a happy, contented horse. When happy, the horse is able to be the best that it can be. "If you listen to the horse, he'll tell you what he wants to do. Then you have to adjust to its schedule," he said. The second element is a strong organization in the shedrow that allows Nafzger and his crew to adapt to the needs of the horse, to become the vehicle for creating a happy, contented horse. "If you can understand them, they'll do okay," Nafzger said more than a year before Unbridled arrived in his barn. "I believe racing is mental. That's where class comes in."

Class is that ultimately undefinable term used so often around the race track. In his book, Nafzger defined what class accomplishes: "Class wins horse races," he wrote. "It is that elusive element that enables a horse to overcome adversity – including trainer and jockey errors, poor track conditions, tough competition, the worst gate position, and getting bumped at the start – and still win. Unbridled had class. It was class that kept him from making mistakes in a race. Unbridled did not make mistakes in any of his races. His trainer did, his jockeys did, and his owners did, but Unbridled made no mistakes." [2]

Nafzger notes, however, that the class horse is not always a champion, as Unbridled was. It very well could be the $5,000 claimer "that you come to love and enjoy just as much because it never lets you down. Running against its peers, it will be the horse that gives you 110 percent and will relish doing battle with all comers in its ability group," he wrote. [3] In short, the class horse is the one that is permitted to be the best that he or she can be.

For the Nafzgers, the people who care for their horses and who manage the grooms and hotwalkers are crucial factors in helping the stable's horses to be everything that they can be. "You've got to teach. You have to get young people who want to learn. Then it's a matter of working with them," he said in early 1988. "Everything came out of the organization. We concentrate as much on our people as on our horses. For us, there is nothing more enjoyable than watching horses develop and people develop and having your owners have fun."

The Derby experience, he said, only emphasized the importance of a strong management structure in the shedrow. He also recognized that the organization he and Wanda had built over two decades deserved much of the credit for the highly successful 1990 campaign. "I realized even more how much this is a people's game, the owners and the people who work for you," he said. "After the Derby, you don't have enough energy or arms to keep up with everything. If you don't build the people, you won't last."

So, what do Carl Nafzger and his horses have to do with substance-abuse problems on North America's race tracks? Horses with class can and will come from all kinds of stables, but they will emerge most often from shedrows that have that indefinable quality: class. Stables that attain the prestige of Carl Nafzger's operation frequently have addressed the problem of alcohol and substance abuse. Some stables have addressed the issue in ways that they may not be fully aware of. If someone comes looking for a job and reeks of alcohol, then that trainer will say, "No, thanks." But Nafzger and others realized that the quality of their stables depends upon the quality of the people they employ, and hiring people with alcohol and drug problems is simply asking for trouble. As in any workplace, the employer is the first-line defense against substance abuse, and on the race track, the trainers are the largest employers.

Sadly, some trainers do not see any connection between their impaired employees and their poor winning record. Others recognize that having impaired employees is bad for their business, and they will shun the drinker and the drug abuser. The reality on the race track, however, is that the drinker fired from one barn will find a job at another with less rigorous standards. With some other top horsemen, Carl Nafzger has adopted a more complex practice, which is rooted in his conviction that a healthy crew produces healthy horses who in turn produce victories. In short, class wins races. To the extent that they can institute it, Nafzger and other trainers have adopted a policy of zero impairment in the workplace. "You have to get the bad element off of your shedrow. But you can't run them off on one or two bad abuses because everybody's going to slip up, mess up, fall off the wagon every now and then," he said. Like many other successful people on the backstretch, Nafzger is an individualist – he has grappled with his own share of personal demons and won. He therefore puts the burden on the individual for turning their lives around: the substance abuser must recognize his or her problem and reach out for help. "We're here to support you," Nafzger said. "We'll back you. But there's only one guy that can help you, and that's yourself."

Would Carl Nafzger ever say that he has attained a workplace that is free of drugs and alcohol? No, not yet. (He is one of those rare individuals who is more concerned with what he is becoming, rather than what he is.) He is enough of a realist to know that he employs people who abuse alcohol and drugs. Once, when the trainer was participating in a track program to reduce substance abuse, a counselor came around to his barn and tacked up a sign that said: "Drug-Free Shedrow." Nafzger asked that the sign be taken down. "One thing I'm not is a liar," Nafzger said. "We know that we have people coming in here with problems. We try to make sure that they don't have those problems when they leave here."

Nafzger presented some of his ideas and strategies for attaining an unimpaired shedrow at the 1990 Conference on Alcohol and Drug Abuse Programs for the Horse Racing Industry, at which he appeared on a panel with W. Cothran "Cot" Campbell, who heads Dogwood Stable. They were rivals on the race track – Unbridled defeated Dogwood's Summer Squall in the 1990 Derby, and Summer Squall turned the tables in the Preakness Stakes two weeks later – but they combined forces at the Louisville Conference to outline ideas for combating the effects of addiction in the racing workplace. Nafzger expanded on some of his management concepts in his book, in a chapter entitled "Good Help a Key Ingredient to Success."

Campbell agreed that the individual must be willing to seek help – must effectively surrender to the addiction and to recovery. He shared with the 1990 Louisville Conference a description of an alcoholic that had been given to him more than three decades earlier. "An alcoholic is like a guy that walks out of his house every morning and he goes through the front gate; and soon as he goes through the gate, a guy jumps out from a bush and beats the hell out of him. And after that happens for about three months, that fellow says, 'Gee, you know, I believe I'd better go out the back door because this is not working well.' And I think that's a good point. I think when people get absolutely fed up with drinking or drug abuse and they can't stand the horrible aftermath of it, that's when they are receptive to doing something about it."

At the Louisville Conference, Nafzger said he and his operation do not look the other way when a person with a problem comes to work for the Nafzgers' Broken N Ranch operation. "We've got three guidelines that we use. We directly acknowledge a problem. As soon as somebody comes on the shedrow that is a substance abuser, we acknowledge the problem," he said at the 1990 Louisville Conference. "Number two, we've got structured work guidelines," he said, "and number three, we provide a lot of incentives for our people. Our shedrow is basically an incentive-driven shedrow."

Nafzger's first principle, as stated in his book, is "know your help." He and Wanda also have rules that are enforced in the workplace. "Not permitted on our shedrow are drinking or drugs. Occasionally we'll host a picnic and buy a case of beer, but we are also well aware that there are people on the backside who are fighting to conquer alcohol problems. We make certain that any gathering has an abundance of soft drinks. Our attitude on alcohol is that we don't mind a person having a mixed drink or a cold beer, we just insist that they don't do so on the shedrow, whether working or visiting. It's a simple but hard and fast rule. No alcohol in the shedrow." [4]

A part of knowing the help is to acknowledge any evidence of substance abuse immediately and directly. "I think the first thing you do, you establish yourself with a sense of trust between the person and yourself or whatever – the barn foreman, my wife, Wanda, the assistant trainer, the co-workers. 'You've got a problem. We know you've got a problem. Now we're not going to jump up here and run you off and fire you because you've got a problem. We're not going to cuss you because you've got a problem. But let's go look at it this way. You've got a problem. We know you've got a problem.' We think it gets rid of some of their sense of guilt of trying to hide the problem. Let's admit it. That's number one," he said.

"Now we take up work guidelines. Our work guidelines are pretty well set. You come to work clean. You do your job. What you do after work is up to you. But evening and afternoon work, if you're disoriented, you're out of it, you're asked to leave. Now, when you leave the shedrow, we do not fire you. Sometimes later that day, sometimes the next day, we talk to this person. To me, one of the most valuable assets we have is communication. We talk to him. We ask him: 'What is wrong with the shedrow? What bothered you? What caused this?' He generally has a problem," Nafzger said. "Maybe it's because of a lot of reasons. What it is, we don't know. Let's find out. We ask these people, 'Why did they come to work in that condition?' They know that that is not what we tolerate. Generally at that time, we get the same run-of-the-mill excuses: you know, so-and-so made me mad last night, I got out, my girlfriend left me, or anything they want to make an excuse. Generally, it's a phony excuse. But sometimes in that conversation, you'll get some good insight. There may be a problem that is really on the shedrow. Maybe his roommate's doing drugs. He got carried away that night. You learn something. At that time you get good insight if you'll listen into the other person's personality, whether he's a liar or whether he's really got a problem or whether he really wants help," Nafzger said at the 1990 Louisville Conference.

One of Nafzger's purposes in meeting with the employee is to establish a sense of trust. "If you get a confidence level going between you and this person, he's got somebody to talk to. You must not become: 'Well, help me, Carl.' No, we do not help you; you help yourself. The thing that we can try to get here is confidence," he said. "Now, if this takes and the person starts going by the guidelines: coming to work clean, coming to work on time . . . then he can go into what we call phase three. He can take on more work." The extra work, which is voluntary, is the means for making additional money and for demonstrating a willingness to progress in the Nafzger workplace. The incentives also are used by Nafzger to battle a problem that is rampant among stable workers: poor self-image. "A lot of these people, in my opinion, have not any self-respect of themselves. If they take a little more work on, they get paid for it. They get a little bonus, but the main thing they get out of it is achievement. They achieved what they wanted. You know: 'By golly, I did it; it's me; it's good.' It's: 'Hey, Carl, did I do a good job?' You did a great job. Now that's what we're looking for right here, a little self-confidence in themselves," he said in 1990. "Now, the thing we're trying to build here is self-respect through achievement. If this takes, you can move on to a little higher. Some of these people went on to be trainers. But, if they keep coming to work and they're not trying, they're lying to you, you got to let them go."

Sometimes, Nafzger said, the confrontation and the firing yield positive results. "A lot of our good employees have been people that have left, then went and cleaned up, and then came back and asked us for a job back; and we've rehired them. They know the system. They know us, and they become good employees."

While Nafzger wants his employees to be the best that they can be, he also recognizes that not all of them will want to be the next Carl Nafzger, or even Nafzger's stable foreman. "We assume that everybody wants the same thing out of life that we want out of life. They don't. They have a pressure level, and we try to find these people where their pressure level's at and just get them happy. We tell them, look, a successful person is a person that is happy achieving what he wishes to achieve. Now if you're happy grooming horses, then that's good. We try to create an environment that you can gain. You can save. We work with saving accounts with these people. We do anything we can. The other thing we encourage is a belief in the Higher Being. We also highly encourage people to join a self-help group such as AA or any self-help group, so that they can get in communication with a friend of their level and their stature that they're comfortable with," he said. At the 1990 Louisville Conference, Nafzger suggested that every race track should have a "clean" dormitory where stable workers who do not wish to be exposed to drugs or alcohol can be housed, and he proposed that every track should have a chapel, a separate building or area where workers can go to meditate and where self-help group meetings can be held in privacy.

Nafzger operates a public stable, in which the trainer has horses of several owners in his shedrow. Cot Campbell's Dogwood Stable, although it turned to public trainers in the late 1980s, once had a private stable with its own trainer in Aiken, South Carolina. They are different operations, but perhaps it is no surprise that both operated with similar work rules. For both, a clean, neat workplace is a top priority. "A clean, neat shedrow will naturally eliminate certain people that you don't want to deal with anyway," Nafzger wrote. "If everyone else is neat and clean, the slob will be out of place and want to be elsewhere, which is just where you want him or her to be." [5]

Campbell said a clean workplace and a clean appearance contribute toward self-esteem. "I believe the biggest contribution to having a barn with a clean and sober environment is to instill a feeling of pride in the employees," he said. "Here are some of the things that we do to try to create a climate where an employee can have some pride and feel good about where he works. We run a smart-looking, clean, attractive barn. We did that when we had the racing stable at the race track, and we do it at our facilities in Aiken, South Carolina. Our people come to work looking good. They're dressed decently. Our riders go out in shirts and helmet covers with our stable colors. And when we first came to Aiken, which we did three years ago (in 1987), having moved there from Atlanta, people made fun of us for doing that. It is interesting to me now that practically all the outfits in Aiken do the same thing. So that's caught on. We don't permit radios in our barn, and we didn't permit it at the race track," he said. "I don't think that the person's use of drugs or alcohol is going to depend on whether he's got a radio in the barn, but it is an example to me of having some rules and running it in a sharp, precise way." Nafzger also prohibits radios and, for safety reasons, radios with earphones. An unimpaired workplace has rules and standards, it is clean and sharp-looking, and it has that undefinable characteristic: class. And, class wins races.

ON THE FARM

Races are also won on the farm. How a horse is raised invariably contributes to – or detracts from – a horse's capability on the track. As with people, the early years are formative, and the maturing runner will benefit from good care and conversely will be impeded by early neglect or abuse – whether intended or unintended. With their attractive country settings, horse farms would not seem to be likely locales for substance abuse. But no area and no workplace is exempt from alcohol and drug problems. In Kentucky alone, the horse-related workplace is very large: it employs or has a direct relationship with 80,000 people, and it accounts for 7 1/2 percent of the state's output of goods and services. The race tracks, while a significant part of the horse industry, are not nearly as large as the state's horse farms. In certain ways, the farm can be a magnet for workers who have worn out their welcome at the race track. John A. Bell III, owner of Jonabell Farm in Lexington, Kentucky, and a Jockey Club member, discussed some of the problems that farms encounter in a session of the 1992 Louisville Conference.

"I'm pretty well convinced that substance abuse is – if it's not the biggest problem we have in the world today – it's right close to it. And for sure, the horse farms face substance-abuse problems just as everyone else does, regardless of what you're involved in. Substance abuse creates the same basic problems on the farm that it does everywhere else. And although the problems on the race track are a lot more dramatic than the ones on the farm, the farm problems are still very, very real," he said. "According to the literature that I have read, approximately 10 percent of the population, or one person in ten, is an alcoholic. An increasingly large number of these alcoholics are recovering alcoholics, thank God. But unfortunately, there are many more who are actively practicing alcoholics. The recovering ones are the ones that are not drinking alcohol, whereas the practicing ones are still drinking and causing many problems for themselves, their families, their employees, and their fellow workers."

Sometimes, these impaired workers move from the race track to the training center or farm. "We get some of them that you might say are running away from the problem, using the geographic cure. They come to the farms and figure, well, we can fool these guys a lot easier than we could at the race track. So we get it, and I think the more the program is working at the race track, the more we're getting it, inheriting it at the farm, because of the fact that it's a little easier to hide at the farm. Because you're dealing with hundreds of acres, they can get lost pretty easily," Bell said.

But people still hit bottom, and Bell said he has confronted impaired long-time employees on a one-to-one basis. In one case, involving a management employee, he offered a choice in the form of two checks. "The one in this hand sends you to Hazelden (the Hazelden Foundation in Center City, Minnesota, a leading inpatient alcoholism-treatment center), for four weeks and buys your airplane ticket, and this one here is your terminal pay, and I don't give a damn which one you take." The employee chose the check for Hazelden.

The farm can be a haven from discovery, as Bell noted, but it also can serve as a haven for recovery. James Day, a leading Canadian trainer, told a story at the 1992 Louisville Conference about a top English-born exercise rider who went to work for him. "He was going to be a major asset to me and my organization, and I couldn't wait to get him involved with some of my horses. And he began with me in Florida on the farm, which is fairly quiet there; and he got along quite well. He got to Keeneland here in the spring; and by the second day we were here, he came to work and he smells a little funny. He isn't talking real clear. And after that day I couldn't get him straight enough where you'd even talk any sense to him. After three or four days in a row, I became very aware of the fact that he was just drunk every day, which really surprised me because he was the only guy in our operation that was that way other than social drinking in the evening. I didn't really have anyone I thought that was a drunk on my payroll," Day said. "I finally got him where I could talk to him and told him, hey, I liked him. I liked his input and I liked his expertise. But, I said, if you can't get yourself straightened up, then I'm not going to be able to keep you, period. So I'll help you, and I'll support you; and we'll get involved immediately in that AA program locally here."

The confrontation worked. "He started to come to work on time and with a clear head. Anyway, once he got into the meetings and the program, he just became so happy and so confident doing that, that he just sort of picked up the ball and started to run with it and couldn't wait to follow up," the trainer said. "And he's become now a very reliable, very clear, sober, good person and a good employee." He also became a nervous exercise rider, which is not a good situation for either the horses or the rider. In all likelihood, the alcohol's impairment had masked his fear of a job at which he was very good. The rider asked to become a groom. "So this fall I had an opportunity that became available at the farm in Florida, and I asked him if he still wanted to try that. I really thought he wouldn't take the opportunity and he'd want to stay riding because it was a much more glamorous job than rubbing horses. But he said, 'Here's my tack, my equipment and my helmet and my spurs and my chaps. You can keep it, and I'm off to Florida. I'm gone tomorrow, and I'm down there.' And he was gone literally two days later," Day said. "He's going to buy a little place in Florida, and he has himself a car, and he's just doing very well, and he's learning to be a groom; and I think, in his situation, I'm very proud of my support and helping him and just sticking behind him."

John Bell conceded that the breeding industry's approach to substance abuse is piecemeal, and he suggested an educational program involving owners, farm managers, or both. "I'm constantly appalled at how few people really understand substance abuse, the problems of addiction; and there are so many misconceptions of it, that I think that education is the place to start," he said. "Now there are many states that have active farm managers clubs. The Kentucky Farm Managers Club has been in existence for about 45 years. I know that because I was one of the guys that started the club, and presently it has a membership of approximately 400 people. That's a lot of people; and it would make sense, I think, to have racing's substance-abuse program contact, as a starting point, contact the Kentucky Farm Managers Club, contact the officers and directors to explore the possibilities of an educational program and attempt to set up a pilot educational program. And a lot of people don't know to get help or where to get it," he said.

An Unimpaired Workforce

Certainly, education is necessary on all levels. A young trainer, in his early 30s, suggested to one of the authors that he thought a jockey was not riding as fearlessly after kicking a drug habit. It is the age-old lie of the race track, that drugs somehow enhance performance. The trainer, who had come up under a Hall of Fame horseman and had the runners of several prominent owners, missed the point that, since getting clean, the jockey may have been riding with better judgment and not taking unnecessary risks – to himself and others. His past "fearlessness" very well may have been recklessness resulting from his impaired judgment. As much as anyone, trainers are hampered by the fictions of the race track: the drugs helped the jockey; the alcoholic was okay in the mornings to rub her horses or to walk them.

That is not intended as a criticism of trainers; rather, as a realization that they are part of the backstretch culture while simultaneously they are fulfilling the real-world role of employer. The trainers are the business people of the backstretch. Each trainer operates his or her own independent business, often within a few feet of a competitor who is in exactly the same business. "There probably is no other business in the world like the horse training business," one trainer said. "It's unique, and it's your life."

A problem common to all trainers is finding and keeping good help. As Carl Nafzger said so succinctly, good help is a key ingredient to success. In this one way, those who train horses for a living have the same problem as any other business person. On any given day at the race track, trainers will complain of a worker who did not show up, one who showed up intoxicated, one who is preoccupied by serious financial or family problems, an employee who came back to the track after developing legal or health problems, or one who was deported. Also, trainers will express genuine distress over a valued employee who became so irritable and ill-tempered that he or she had to be let go. After all, good help is hard to find.

Trainers invariably tell you that times have changed, that the people who worked for them in the "old days" did not have these problems and that today's employees are unwilling to work as hard. In all likelihood, the overall character of the work force has not changed; but perhaps the worker pool of the race track has. In fact, the "good help" problem is not what it appears to be. Perhaps, because of the ease with which unskilled workers can enter and move about in the stable-area workplace, the race track has an impairment problem. As national pollster George Gallup Jr. suggested: "America does not have a crime problem. America does not have a problem of job absenteeism and low productivity. America does not have a teenage pregnancy problem. America does not have a problem of broken homes and marriages. America has an alcohol and drug problem." Certainly, the race track has a problem with alcoholism and drug abuse, and on the backstretch this problem most acutely affects the trainers, who need "good help" to operate their businesses.

In some cases, the trainers may not even be aware that their workers are impaired. But, if the impairment exists, in time it will surface. There is a hard, fast rule about how alcohol and drug problems show in the workplace. The rule can be remembered by the acronym "TELL," as in "the disease will TELL us what the truth is." "TELL" stands for "Tight Early, Loose Late." Early in the process of problem drinking or abuse of illegal drugs, the "user" is careful to put up a good front to keep from being detected. The abuser will show up for work on time almost always, and he or she will have almost believable explanations for their absences and lapses. These abusers are "tight;" their priority, after their substance abuse, is to "look okay," and they will function in their jobs despite the effort that they must expend to do so. After a while, however, the disease takes its inevitable toll, and it begins to "tell the truth" about what is going on. The tight controls begin to relax or fail, and steadily the picture begins to emerge until it is undeniable. The problem drinker, alcoholic, or drug user becomes "loose." Absent, late, hung over, injured, in trouble, slow, or even dangerous to self or others, the user does not have the energy to cover up any more; they surrender to the roles that go with drug- or alcohol-induced impairment. Being called lazy, no good, a wino, a drunk, an alkie – or anything else – matters little to the person as long as they have work of some kind. Without work, they have no resources to buy their drugs or alcohol, and so work "goes last." Tight Early, Loose Late.

Are the race track's abusers different from those in other businesses and industries? Perhaps so, perhaps not. No studies have been conducted that would answer that question conclusively. But certainly trainers have seen the effects of impairment, which show up in well-known but costly ways. As compared to unimpaired workers, substance abusers:

☐ Are less productive at work.

☐ Are absent from work more often.

☐ Are more likely to injure themselves or someone else, both on and off the job.

☐ File more worker's compensation claims.

That last factor is more than enough reason for an employer to attack the problem. What businessperson can afford to have worker's compensation claims increased even a small amount?

For the longest time, North America's trainers have tended to throw up their hands and say, in effect, that the drunks and drug abusers will always be with us. For the individual trainer – and this is a business problem that must be attacked on a business-by-business basis – there is an answer. Nancy Reagan told America to just say no to drugs. On the race track, it is the trainer who must say no to impairment, and the answer is much simpler than it used to be. The answer is to establish a drug-free workplace. For trainers at one of the 54 race tracks with on-track substance-abuse programs, solving the "good-help" problem begins with a call to that program. Then, with most of the work being done by the on-track substance-abuse program, the trainer need only follow a step-by-step guideline published by the U.S. Department of Labor, "What Works: Workplaces Without Alcohol and Other Drugs." This publication, which is available free from the National Clearinghouse for Alcohol and Drug Information and through the on-track programs, even provides a sample written policy statement that the trainer may follow as closely as he or she chooses.

The publication tells "top management" to address the problem, and on the backstretch there is no question about who "top management" is. It's the trainer, whether he or she has five horses or one hundred horses. Simply put, the drug-free workplace is a leadership or management function, and it happens only if management says it will happen. The trainer first must make the decision to have a drug-free workplace and then must stick to that decision.

Thereafter, things fall into place without too much difficulty, at least for trainers who are on one of the 54 race tracks that have on-track substance-abuse programs. The trainer puts the following elements in place:

1. A written substance-abuse policy.
2. An employee education and awareness program.
3. A supervisor-training program for those who oversee other workers within the trainer's organization.
4. An employee assistance program.
5. A drug testing program, if appropriate.

The sample written policy – some examples are in the Labor Department publication and another was developed by the President's Drug Advisory Council – can be copied or modified by the trainer. The second, third, and fourth items should be readily available to the trainer from the on-track substance-abuse program. Establishing a drug-testing program requires a bit more care, but it is not really difficult or a financial burden. Legal advice, given the various state statutes, is a proper precaution. In many cases, the race track's retained attorney may provide that help because the track will clearly benefit from the trainer's initiative. Here are some general ideas that should be checked out with appropriate legal counsel.

First, the trainer should be aware that the Americans With Disabilities Act of 1990 prohibits discrimination against qualified people with disabilities and also limits what can be asked about a job applicant's or an employee's medical history. It does not preclude drug testing, and it does allow the employer to prohibit alcohol abuse or illegal drug use in the workplace. State laws vary and, of course, the trainer would want to check on local laws that may govern the drug-free workplace provisions. However, the essence of the law's provision is that those who are in recovery and are free of alcohol and drugs cannot be refused employment solely on the basis of their substance-abuse history.

Second, the trainer should know about the Drug-Free Workplace Act of 1988. This applies to federal-grant recipients and federal contractors where the contract exceeds $25,000. It is not likely to apply directly to the horse-racing industry, but it forms the logical basis for some state laws dealing with a drug-free workplace and drug testing in the workplace, including laws for those states that restrict drug testing, such as Iowa and Rhode Island. The recommended elements of a drug-free workplace, as described above, are required by the Drug-

Free Workplace Act of 1988.

Third, drug-testing technology has come a long way in the past five or so years. While drug testing previously was a long, drawn-out procedure in which considerable time elapsed between testing and results, drug testing can now be done on the spot and very simply. The new technology is ELISA, or "enzyme-linked immunoabsorbent assay" technique. These techniques provide results in eight to ten minutes and are highly reliable. Confirmation with more traditional tests can be done if called for by company policy (the policy adopted by the trainer) when a positive result occurs.

Simply having the ELISA test available and demonstrating its use to employees as part of the education and prevention effort can reduce substance abuse. "Recreational users" are often deterred by the fear of detection, while addicts or alcoholics are not deterred. The trainer's policy can specify what "probable-cause" behaviors in the workplace will result in testing. However, when the supervisor has probable cause, there can be considerable advantage in allowing the employee to do the test personally, under surveillance. Often, knowing that he or she is "dirty," the employee does not take the test and stipulates that drugs are in his or her system. The trainer can then act according to company policy.

Now we get to the hard part. While few will argue that illegal drugs such as cocaine, crack, or heroin are problem drugs that have no place on the backstretch, many draw the line at considering beer or other alcoholic drinks as problems. But it is a problem, big time. To be sure, alcohol is legal and it certainly is socially acceptable across social classes. Further, the U.S. has behind it a failed experiment with prohibition, and there is no support for repeating that experiment. Banning beer from the backstretch has been done at some tracks, but even there it is more likely that the ban is on visible alcohol, not on alcohol itself. Out of sight, out of mind.

What is not debatable is that alcohol is the most-abused drug in our society, and it is the one that is most costly for the horse-racing industry and other industries. Its effects on the trainer may be direct or indirect. For example, an entire Friday evening's race card at one major track was jeopardized when an intoxicated tractor driver backed into a light pole. On the pole was the transformer that provided power to the track! By luck, a power-company repair team was close to the track, and that night's races and purses were saved. Or consider the scene at a Midwest race track, where a groom was so intoxicated in the test barn after a race that she was all but carried along by the horse. A dozen or so persons were watching, and so was a security guard. Nobody acted. What would have happened if the horse broke loose from her tenuous grasp on both consciousness and the shank, resulting in injury to horses or people? How large would the lawsuit or lawsuits be? Who would pay this cost of alcohol abuse?

The second difficult aspect of dealing with alcohol abuse is the backstretch's dual function as workplace and residence. Much like a military base, the race track boundary defines both a place of work and a self-contained living space. They overlap. Does it make sense to ban a legal substance, used moderately, from a person's dwelling when he or she is not on duty? Probably not.

The way out of this dilemma is simple but somewhat difficult. The trainer, as employer, has to define the conditions of employment that are acceptable. The first rule is "no impairment" due to even small amounts of alcohol in the system. That puts the emphasis on fitness for work, and disregards when or where alcohol was used. A hangover that causes tardiness or absenteeism is treated in the same way as sucking on a half pint while walking a horse. Taking a "beer break" at the track kitchen before the afternoon feeding can be defined as unacceptable if the trainer wishes to do that. The point here is that the trainer is in control and, if working together, trainers can be in control of what's acceptable regarding alcohol use on the backstretch.

Alcoholism is a progressive but fatal disease, and employers in the past have frequently postponed action, hoping against hope that the problem will clear itself up. Sometimes, no doubt, this acquiescence to addiction has at least kept a worker available, whereas dealing with the problem would have meant firing the problem worker, with no chance of soon picking up as good a worker as a replacement. Because of this attitude, some racetrackers describe having stayed in this cycle for decades as they moved from barn to barn and from track to track. Someone was always desperate enough, or gullible enough, to hire them.

Establishing a drug-free workplace, while not arduous or time-consuming for a trainer or other employer, can pay off handsomely. First, by working with an on-track substance-abuse program to establish the policy, the trainer obtains a resource – something to turn to when a trusted employee runs into alcohol or drug problems. No longer would it be necessary to tell the employee to pack up and ship out. If the trainer chooses to do so, he or she can turn to the on-track program for rehabilitation opportunities – a way to make an employee productive again. Many on-track programs provide help for problems other than substance abuse, such as marital or financial counseling. If used as soon as the problem is identified, the on-track substance-abuse program can keep the employee at work while effective treatment proceeds. The trainer both corrects a serious problem and keeps the worker on the job.

The second advantage for the trainer is the gain of a grateful, recovering employee. This "attitude of gratitude" produces an exceptionally hard-working, reliable, and productive employee who gets even better with time. Loyalty to the "company" that provides the help is remarkable and pays dividends to the employer. Money can't buy that sort of commitment.

Finally, the drug-free workplace saves money because it is safer and has fewer time-lost accidents both on and off of the job. There are fewer reasons for worker's compensation claims and medical-insurance claims, and the savings are obvious. Do large companies institute employee-assistance programs out of any sense of altruism? Usually, no. They know – they have hard data – that they make more money with an unimpaired work force. And some states and insurance companies have begun to give financial breaks to companies, including racing stables, that institute drug-free workplaces. Florida, for example, gives a premium discount to trainers who have a drug-free workplace. Moreover, an impairment-free workplace puts the stable's attention on winning, which is the name of this game. Class wins races. And recovering people win races, too.

1. Carl A. Nafzger, Traits of a Winner: The Formula for Developing Thoroughbred Racehorses (Neenah, Wisconsin: Russell Meerdink Company, 1994.
2. Ibid, page 17.
3. Ibid, page 17-18.
4. Ibid, page 209-210.
5. Ibid, page 199.

Chapter 8

Backstretch Pioneers

Programs for alcohol and drug abuse did not begin with Jim Ryan, the Ryan Family Foundation, or the Conference on Alcohol and Drug Abuse Programs for the Horse Racing Industry. In fact, the Ryan Foundation's efforts began in direct response to a pioneering initiative at Maryland's race tracks, and the Louisville Conference was necessitated by the growing number of treatment programs on North America's race tracks. Even before Maryland's program began, individuals such as Louis R. Rowan in California and Lucy Reum in Illinois were acting to launch innovative programs in their home areas. Illinois's initiative was so radical that it will be discussed in a separate chapter.

THE CALIFORNIA EXPERIENCE

Lou Rowan died in 1988, and his obituary in *The Blood-Horse* outlined many facets of a fascinating life. Born to wealth in Southern California and educated in Europe, he loved horse racing and was deeply involved in the sport in Southern California. An original stockholder in Santa Anita Park, he was a founding member of the Oak Tree Racing Association and served as secretary-treasurer of the Del Mar Thoroughbred Club. President of the California Thoroughbred Breeders Association from 1955 through 1960, he bred and was the co-owner of Quicken Tree, winner of the 1968 Jockey Club Gold Cup over champion Damascus.

Rowan's obituary also noted briefly that he was a founder of the Winners Foundation in California and that he was a supporter of the Bishop Gooden Home for business and professional people recovering from alcoholism. The industry tribute did not note, however, that Rowan was himself a recovering alcoholic. "One of the things that happened for Lou Rowan was that he got sober," said the Rev. John Mayton, who served as the second director of the Winners Foundation program. "When he got sober, he began to look at the world that he loved, the horse racing world, and he got real concerned about the conditions there. For many years, Lou Rowan would reach into his own pocket and pay the way into treatment for people. He would sponsor a lot of people. Here's this man with awesome wealth who was sponsoring grooms and hotwalkers and jockeys and mutuel clerks and people like that," Mayton said at the first Louisville Conference in 1989. "But his dream was to have something at the race track that would do this, a program at the race track that would address alcohol and drug problems." In 1984, with financial assistance from Oak Tree, Santa Anita, and Del Mar and with support from the California Horsemen's Benevolent and Protective Association, the Winners Foundation was formally launched. The Winners Foundation came into existence in large part because Rowan was an insider who perceived a need within the racing community and was able to influence his peers to ally themselves with the effort. Rowan's dream soon ran into difficulty because its first director became fatally ill, and the Winners Foundation drifted. Mayton, a recovering alcoholic and drug addict who served as chaplain at Longacres Racetrack in Washington, was brought in to get the Winners Foundation going again. At first, the Winners Foundation was Mayton, a recovering jockey who was hired at the new director's insistence, and a tiny trailer on the backstretch at Santa Anita. "That's how we started out, and we began to implement our program. The philosophy of the program was, anyone in racing and their families who have drug and alcohol problems, we were there to help, and it doesn't cost anything. Our program was free to the people who came to it," Mayton said in 1989, when he was working for the Ryan Family Foundation to finance substance-abuse programs on 54 North American race tracks.

Mayton, like others in the field, found that people were not immediately beating down his door. For the sake of his reports to the Winners Foundation board, Mayton engaged in some creative calculations. "I wanted to look good when I first got down there, and what I call hard clients, ones that are referred to me, I didn't have a whole bunch of those. I had a couple, but not a whole bunch. So I began to note everybody who came in the office, and I had to get creative about the headings that I put them underneath," Mayton said, so he created the category of 'supportive clients.' "Those were the folks who were using the Winners Foundation as a part of their program of recovery. They might not be seeing us formally, but they were showing up off and on, and hanging out, and drinking our coffee, and researching their lives with us, or whatever. Whatever they were doing, if they were showing up, they got down on the piece of paper," he said.

Referrals increased, though, when he established a relationship with the track's security officers. "I went to security at Santa Anita race track and said: 'This is what I do, and this is how I do it. This is what I'd like to do. How can I work with you?' Security says: 'That's wonderful. We'd really like to have that here, the drug and alcohol program. Our concern is that if we send somebody over to you who is a problem for us, that we have some sort of assurance that they are going to be there getting better. Or if they're not there, we need to know, because we still have the problem if they're not going to get better.' So I said: 'Okay, this is what you can do. If you're going to send somebody to me, call me and let me know that they're coming, and if after a certain period of time they don't show up, I'll call you back and say they didn't show up. Secondly, if they enter into the program, I will not be able to tell you what we talk about inside that room. However, I will be able to tell you if they complete the program, and I'll let you know if for some reason they are not going to continue with the program, whether they are going to move to another race track, or whether they're not showing up, or whether they told me to go screw myself, or whatever. I'll let you know that,' " Mayton said.

"That worked pretty well. We had to do a little adjusting around that, because sometimes somebody wouldn't show up for a scheduled counseling session, and I had to have a little elbow room. I had to go out and maybe shake a bar stool or something to get them back into the fold, or maybe their trainer sent them over to another track to do something with a horse, and they couldn't make it, and they couldn't get in touch with me."

By enlisting security's assistance, Mayton established a rudimentary tracking system. "If we had somebody that wasn't going to play ball with us and they would do a little geographic cure and go to another race track, I would call security and say: 'Fritz has decided he doesn't want to participate in the Winners Foundation program, and he is leaving the race track.' They didn't participate, and they had to leave. So security would write a letter to Hollywood Park, to their counterpart at Hollywood Park, and say: 'Our ruling at Santa Anita was that this individual had to participate in the Winners Foundation program, and he's no longer participating in it.' So when Fritz would arrive at Hollywood Park, he might get in the gate, and he might get himself a job, but sooner or later he would get himself into trouble, or he'd get spotted by a security officer, or something. They'd bring him in, and they'd say: 'Listen, Fritz, you haven't completed your program over at Santa Anita. What are you doing here?' Fritz would get all upset and either come back and finish up with us or go to another race track. Pretty soon, because our program expanded all throughout California, there was no place to go except Pomona. It got real crazy at Pomona (Fairplex Park of the Los Angeles County Fair Association), because everybody who wouldn't play ball at the five major race tracks ended up at Pomona, and that's where all the drunks and addicts were, the ones that were really active in their addiction. That's where they ended up," Mayton said. Eventually, even the fair tracks, including Pomona, began to participate in the Winners Foundation program.

At the insistence of the HBPA, the Winners Foundation trailer moved from Santa Anita to Hollywood Park, where the management at that time did not want the program. After the Hollywood spring meet, Mayton and his team moved to Del Mar, which he described as an eye-opening experience. "People said, 'You'll get a lot of clients down at Del Mar.' They were right, but we didn't get them in Del Mar. We got them after Del Mar, because the Del Mar race meet was just this insane party. I mean, the last year I was down at Del Mar, we lost four people to overdoses. They party down. They go down there, and everybody relaxes, and they kick back, and there's a lot of money, and it's a short race meet, and it's in a party town," he said. "But the result of that was that a lot of people got really sick really fast, and when we went back up to Santa Anita for the Oak Tree meet, I got overloaded. We had some sick puppies coming through our door, and by then we had made the full Southern California circuit, and we were now a part of horse racing. Security was comfortable with us, and the stewards were comfortable with us, and I did things like steward seminars."

At one point during his tenure, though, Mayton said he made a serious mistake: as the program grew larger, he forgot who his clients were. With the trailer packed with substance abusers and people in recovery, he started to believe that they were the clients, when in fact his most important constituency was the board of directors that had hired him, the race-track management, and the trainers. "My real client was the industry, and I forgot that. When I first went there, I knew who my client was, it was the industry, and I acted as if that were true and related to the industry as a client. They were special, they had needs, and I began to address those needs in that way. As a result of that, they sent me a lot of people, and so I changed my focus from an industry to individual counseling," he said. "But what I was there, in reality, to do was to treat an industry. When I wasn't busy with folks on the frontside and talking with management and getting around to the HBPA office and getting over into security, these kinds of places, they didn't know where I was at." Mayton verbalized a problem that has plagued substance-abuse programs on the race track. While it is very easy and comforting to counsel clients, the real work is often done on the frontside, in the offices of the people who pay the bills and who need to be reminded on a regular basis that the treatment programs are cost-effective ways of increasing the efficiency of the backstretch and the race track itself.

After Mayton's departure to work with the Ryan Family Foundation, the Winners Foundation's work continued in earnest. Leslie Martin, who served as the Winners Foundation's executive director beginning in mid-1989, presented a statistical profile of the program at the 1990 Louisville Conference. Its budget was $220,000 in the preceding year, and the program had undergone robust growth with the infusion of Ryan Foundation money. "I think the Ryan Foundation money seeded our growth to a great degree," he said. In October 1990, with seven full-time employees, the Winners Foundation had 89 clients, with 37 of them regarded as current clients. "I guess about two-thirds of them are sent by stewards, the security, and track management; and about a third of them come in on their own because of the publicity and the knowledge and our long-term presence on the track," Martin said. Into the mid-1990s, Richard D. Smith served as president of the Winners Foundation's board of directors. A decade after its founding by Lou Rowan, the Winners Foundation remained an important part of the California racing scene.

THE MARYLAND EXPERIENCE

The Winners Foundation got up and running because of Lou Rowan's vision and his clout within the California industry. The Maryland program, created by the industry and operated by an academic organization, entered the public's consciousness because of a drug abuser from the wrong side of the tracks. But this was no ordinary substance abuser. Ronnie Franklin had reached for the stars astride a gray lightning bolt – Spectacular Bid – who was described by his trainer as "the best horse ever to look through a bridle." On the Meyerhoff family's Bid, the kid from hard-scrabble Dundalk – Baltimore's gritty dock area – had risen to the heights of the sport, gaining an Eclipse Award as 1978's champion apprentice jockey. Franklin was like a son to trainer Grover G. 'Bud' Delp, and they sometimes spatted like father and son. Delp delivered a verbal horse whipping to the young rider after he found more than enough ways to get Bid beat in the 1979 Florida Derby – but the steel-gray wonder won despite his rider's worst efforts. Delp was inundated with coast-to-coast pleas to take Franklin off this super horse, but after long deliberation decided to keep him on Bid. Together after that, Franklin rode Spectacular Bid to victories in the Flamingo Stakes and the Blue Grass Stakes, and the Bid team was the toast of Louisville before the 105th Kentucky Derby on May 5, 1979. Bid lined up against some very nice horses such as General Assembly and Flying Paster, but he rolled over them, winning the Run for the Roses by nearly three lengths. On home ground at Pimlico Race Course for the Preakness two weeks later, Spectacular Bid was beyond spectacular, opening six lengths in mid-stretch and winning by 5 1/2 lengths over Golden Act. Then came the Belmont and the prospect of a third Triple Crown winner in three years, after Seattle Slew in 1977 and Affirmed in 1978. But Spectacular Bid did not have enough staying power in his pedigree to get 1 1/2 miles, and he finished third to Coastal. At the time, Delp attributed the loss to a bandage pin that had penetrated Spectacular Bid's left foot in his stall on the morning of the race, and others said that Franklin had gone to the lead too soon. But the simple fact was that Spectacular Bid was not going to get 1 1/2 miles over a Belmont Park track known as "big sandy." If his pedigree did not stop him, certainly the arduous Triple Crown campaign did.

But someone had to pay the price, and it was the 19-year-old Franklin who was sacrificed on the altar of public disappointment. Replacing him was the ageless Bill Shoemaker, a Hall of Fame member who rode the colt through the remainder of his career, including Bid's unbeaten Horse of the Year campaign in 1980. Franklin, without the big horse, drifted toward obscurity as a young apprentice jockey, Julieann Krone, arrived at the Delp barn. Franklin had always been the subject of rumors that he had a drug problem, and he was ruled off in 1986 for a positive drug test. Another career, it appeared, had skyrocketed and crashed.

At about the same time, the Maryland backstretch counseling program had been established at the state's two remaining mile tracks, Pimlico and Laurel Park, and at Bowie Race Course, which had been closed and transformed into a training facility. Franklin and the program would eventually enter into a mutually beneficial relationship. Franklin would enter treatment and ultimately return to the track; the program headed by Bob Babes would get the attention it needed to become a factor on the Maryland tracks.

For the longest time, Bob Babes thought that the nascent program was not succeeding. He was doing everything that he thought he should do, but few clients were being referred to him, and he was playing a lot of golf. The program was created by the Maryland Horsemen's Assistance Fund, a nonprofit organization whose roots reached back more than a half century and whose efforts were paid, in part, by fines collected by the Maryland Racing Commission. In 1985, the Maryland fund sought proposals for a substance-abuse program, and the winning bidder was the University of Maryland Alcohol and Drug Abuse Program. Babes, who had been working in a Methadone clinic, agreed to take the assignment, and the Maryland program began in February 1986.

One of the first lessons he learned, he said at the 1989 Louisville Conference, was that he needed a pair of rubberized mud shoes to cope with the backstretch environment, where washing and hosing of horses' legs created perpetually muddy conditions. The mud, though, was the least of his problems. "That was the hardest time for me," he said. "For the first six or eight months, something like that, I didn't stay very busy." Even before that, Babes had sensed that his task would be difficult. Although the Horsemen's Assistance Fund had set up the program, he sensed that strong support for the initiative was not unanimous on the board, or even a plurality. "They were a bit guarded. Really, there were I believe eight people on the board, and there were only two who were really sensitive to trying to get the program going. The other six or so were fairly in denial that there was a problem, probably due to their own issues. That's a social-work thought on the issues back there. Anyway, Jim Ryan came into the picture early on and said he would kick in some money. So I've known Jim for a long time. That helped the other six to comply, because they tend to focus on money. We explained to them what we were going to do. We were going to implement an EAP (employee-assistance program)," he said. "After that, I came on the race track four days later, and I had all these ideas and all these plans. I set up meetings with people to explain what we were going to do. I think we had a series of five meetings, which I think was real important because we got representatives from the stewards, representatives from the racing commission, representatives from the security department, representatives from management, our nurse, and some board members, and the horsemen's organization."

An employee-assistance-program specialist explained to them how the program would work. "We explained to them all these statistics about industry, about how alcohol and drug abuse affects a certain percentage of the population and how much money they lose on absenteeism, all these things. I just sat there, and it was really wild, because it was really the first time I had really, really heard it. I had read about it; she gave me the literature. She did a really good job, and she showed how we could really improve the industry by helping those people on the race track, primarily people on the backside. She was a moving lady; she had people looking at this. A problem occurred. She quit the next month. The director of the drug-treatment center I worked at quit the next month. So I was left there with an EAP program that I didn't know how the hell to run," Babes said.

"One of our ideas was to hang posters. What I did was walk the barns and I hung a poster such as: "Asking for help is a sign of courage." Because the race track did not want to see anything about alcohol or drug abuse on any of the posters. They were afraid it would scare people," he said. "I walked shedrows for about two months, hanging and rehanging the posters, and rehanging. I was told a year or so ago that a lot of my posters were in people's rooms. They'd just hang them in their rooms." Like Mayton before him, Babes counted the tracks' recovering people among his clients, just to show that he indeed had clients."I probably didn't get a client for almost two months," he said. "As I walked the barns, I saw this stuff that was going on. I said we need something back here. This place is weird. I had never been back there. These guys, it's 7 o'clock in the morning and they're drinking scotch." When Babes finally got a client, the man died of his alcoholism. "He developed pneumonia, his lungs filled, and he tried to medicate himself with scotch, and he died in his room. I was feeling kind of bad. I was playing a lot of golf because I refused to sit in that damned office and just sit there and look at the stuff. I tried to walk around, but after 11 o'clock you don't see anyone. They're all on the frontside by now or in their rooms. I was kind of lost. So, I said, I guess I have to advertise more," Babes said. "What I did was to go and talk to the people who fund the program, the Horsemen's Assistance Fund, and asked them if I could make up another poster. They said: 'Well, I don't know.' This was after three months, four months, I guess. I told them what I wanted to do. I wanted to start talking about the fact that there is an alcohol- and drug-abuse problem on the race track, and I wanted people to see that there was in a big, bright picture. I had *High Times* magazines from the good old days. So I found a picture in there, and what I decided to do was to make another poster."

The posters, plastered up all over the three tracks, appeared to be a big hit. "Well, they started disappearing, and I thought, this is good. I thought they were connecting, but then again I'd find them in the trash cans or people said they were hanging in rooms, because they were pretty nice-looking posters. I'd find them, and the bottom would be cut off. The top says: 'Drugs.' The bottom says: 'Will kill, will not be tolerated on the Maryland race tracks, will cause you to lose your racing commission license and all privileges. Call the Horsemen's Counseling Program for confidential help.' I started finding the bottoms all over the place, but I never found the tops," he said. "I said, this isn't working. I know they're seeing it, but they're not coming to see me. So I need to do something else. I've gone on now probably four months, and I've probably seen ten people maybe, and they didn't really come and see me consistently."

It was then that Babes decided to solicit referrals from the stewards. He spent considerable time with Maryland's stewards as well as members of the racing commission. "I would go to see the head of security every day and talk to him on each race track. I would drive all around. I spent an enormous amount of time talking to security, stewards, racing commission, and trainers. The trainers were a little tougher," Babes said. "But after about six months, people were starting to come, people were starting to refer people." Babes's next step was be make the program a part of the disciplinary system. "I said to the stewards: 'Hey, when you get these people into the stewards, when you're having a hearing, why don't you directly refer them to me? That's why I'm here,' " he said.

The stewards resisted initially, but then Ronnie Franklin came into the program in late 1986, after he had been suspended for a marijuana positive. "I worked real hard with him, I saw him like three times a week. I did like three urines a week on him, and it was his second offense, but he had a lot of legal problems," said Babes, who did not identify Franklin by name at the 1989 Louisville Conference. To be sure, many within Maryland racing wished that Babes would not bother with Franklin. "He was a total embarrassment to the race track. They just disliked him. He was from a section of town that people didn't think was too cool, and commissioners tend to sit up a little high. They really thought he was a waste. Anyway, we got him back, and they made him an exercise rider for six months. He did well, and I was in contact with the commission. The commission hearing was a gas. They grilled me for about two and a half hours, district attorney-style," Babes said. Franklin was, with restrictions, granted an exercise rider's license on April 2, 1987, and he was reinstated as a jockey on July 10 of that year. The license had two restrictions: Franklin had to be off the race track by sundown, and he had to continue counseling.

Franklin's return to the track was excellent marketing for the program. "They plastered it all over the newspapers and got my name all over the newspaper," Babes said. "I started coming up with all these magazines, I saved this famous jock, and I started to get a lot of referrals. I said, 'Wait a second.' That flabbergasted me. What they were waiting for was to see if I could do anything, whether I could do any work." He also had turned a blight on the industry, a story about a drug-abusing jockey, into a positive one, a rider who cleans up his act and returns to the racing.

"After that happened, there was an immense influx of clients. After that happened, there was an immense urinalysis testing that took place on the backside of the race track. They started banging barns. They had people flying over to me," Babes said. "I think what happened was that the publicity got people to realize that we need to do something about what is going on." Soon, Babes had a full caseload composed principally of backstretch workers who had come to the program voluntarily. Ronnie Franklin, who had played a role in the early success of Spectacular Bid, also had a significant role in the earliest success of the Maryland treatment program. Within a year of the first Louisville Conference, Babes left for an out-of-state job opportunity, and his work was carried forward into the mid-1990s by Anthony Schefstad. In both California and Maryland, pioneering efforts have grown and matured from the mid-1980s into the middle of the 1990s.

Chapter 9

My Old Kentucky Home

Few moments in sports compare to that magical instant when the horses come onto Churchill Downs' track for the Kentucky Derby. For many in the crowd of more than 100,000 on the glorious first Saturday in May, it is a highly emotional time as the Derby horses – who are only a few minutes away from fame or ignominy – make the left-hand turn up the homestretch to the strains of "My Old Kentucky Home." For at least one horse and owner on that fading afternoon, the sun will indeed shine bright.

Paul C. McDonald Jr. has been a part of this world – the world of Churchill Downs – for all of his life. His father, Paul McDonald Sr., was an assistant to the legendary Colonel Matthew Winn, the racing impresario who made the Derby into the world's most famous horse race. In the mid-1920s, Winn dispatched his executive to Illinois to open and operate Lincoln Fields, a race track 30 miles from Chicago and now known as Balmoral. From his earliest days, Paul McDonald Jr. knew the glory of the Derby and of Thoroughbred racing. And, as a youngster in the late 1930s at Lincoln Fields, he came face to face with the racing world's darker reality. One ghastly vision, in particular, forever left its mark on him and led to creation of Churchill Downs's Lifestyle Program a half-century later. Paul McDonald Jr. resolved that, if he were ever in a position to do something to improve backstretch living conditions, he would not shrink from doing so. A man of his word, McDonald put his resolve into action.

The younger McDonald was a race track brat, and he accompanied his father as he traveled the frontside and backside of Lincoln Fields. The elder McDonald had many race track friends, and he and young

Paul would often stop to visit with a favorite trainer to talk about racing. During one of the visits, the trainer was found collapsed in a stall, vomiting his life blood into the bedding straw of one of his runners.

The young child watched in horror as blood poured from the man's mouth, as the trainer's life seeped through the mat of bedding and into the race track's soil. "I saw this man bleed to death in the straw," Paul McDonald Jr. said in 1995. "He collapsed in the straw and started hemorrhaging. They didn't have any ambulances then like they do now. He bled to death right there," he said. "It shook me. That stuck with me."

In time, the elder McDonald told his son that the trainer had died of alcoholism. Presumably, the bleeding was caused was esophageal varices, a condition that, like cirrhosis of the liver, is often associated with alcoholism. The type of death that McDonald witnessed may have been out of the ordinary, but the alcoholism was commonplace. "You see that all the time," said the younger McDonald, who also saw clearly from a young age that race track living conditions – even in what some people fantasize was the "golden age" of horse racing – were beyond deplorable. "You talk about the backside of a circus. They had dirt floors. It was horrible. There weren't any johns or showers. You heated the tack rooms with an L & N (Louisville and Nashville Railroad) caboose stove," he said.

McDonald served in the Navy, returned to Louisville to get his undergraduate degree from the University of Louisville, and worked part-time at Churchill Downs to keep in touch with his first love, Thoroughbred racing. When the opportunity to establish a new position to improve the track's relationship with its horsemen presented itself, McDonald put aside his sales career and took it. In time, he reached a position of authority, as interim general manager, in 1984. He was thrown into the breach in one of the darkest times in Churchill's history as an ill-conceived summer racing schedule sapped the track's financial strength, and takeover vultures circled around the dowager track. Shortly after taking his first full-time position with Churchill, McDonald suggested to a senior manager that the track should institute some sort of backstretch program to deal with the hooch and hop. The former manager "looked at me like I had three heads," McDonald said.

That attitude toward backstretch programs, and many other aspects of race track management changed, however, when Warner L. Jones Jr. took over as chairman from the ailing John W. Galbreath. Jones was, in a phrase, a giant of the Kentucky Turf. Although his Hermitage Farm was located northeast of Louisville and far from the famous farms of Lexington's Bluegrass, Jones was a formidable player in the rough-and-tumble world of horse trading and was widely respected within the industry. His associations with Churchill went back to the track's very beginnings. His great-great-grandmother was a Churchill, whose name is associated with the track because members of the family leased the South Louisville site to Colonel M. Lewis Clark, the track's founder and Jones's great-great-uncle. Warner Jones watched his first Derby in 1930 when Belair Stud's Gallant Fox began his Triple Crown sweep, and he became a Churchill director in 1941 at age 25.

Six years earlier, Jones had founded Hermitage with $50,000 borrowed from his mother. By the time of his death in early 1994, Warner Jones had bred no fewer than 131 stakes winners and had accomplished a notable triple. He bred and sold a Derby winner, Dark Star in 1953 (the only blemish on Native Dancer's record); a Kentucky Oaks winner, Nancy Jr. in 1967; and a Breeders' Cup championship winner, Is It True, who defeated juvenile champion Easy Goer in the Breeders' Cup championship run at Churchill in 1988. Among the other top horses that he bred were leading sires Woodman and Rousillon.

Warner Jones also was a founder, in 1943, of the Breeders' Sales Company, which would become the Keeneland Sales, and he was co-breeder of the most expensive yearling ever sold, $13.1-million in 1985 for a Nijinsky II colt, Seattle Dancer, who was a half brother to 1977 Triple Crown winner Seattle Slew. Jones was just as perceptive about the need for the horse industry to develop a national presence in Washington and to monitor new legislation affecting the industry. To make this happen, he became one of the founders of the American Horse Council.

A lesser known fact was that Jones had been sober for some 40 years, and he shared McDonald's concern about alcoholism in the racing community. But first priority went to the task of renewing Churchill

Downs, which, Jones saw, had become dingy and demoralized. While Paul McDonald served as interim general manager, Jones tapped Thomas H. Meeker, the lawyer who had erected Churchill's corporate-takeover defenses, to be the track's president in 1984. "Meeker came on board, and I said, 'Tom, we have to do something on this backside.' Drugs and prostitution were rampant," McDonald said. Indeed, McDonald was able to clear some of the troublemakers out of the backstretch before Gerald Lawrence, general manager of Yonkers Raceway, was named to be Churchill's general manager later in 1984. McDonald accepted the task of rehabilitating Churchill's position with the Kentucky Legislature, as a lobbyist, but he remained just as determined to do something about the conditions on the backstretch and the alcoholism found there. McDonald had not forgotten that one too many of his friends, a racetracker, had bled his life into the soil of a racetrack.

With a $25-million remodeling program, Churchill Downs rebuilt itself, and it also rebuilt its customer service and marketing. As some of the clouds over the financial landscape began to clear, an opportunity arose to do something substantial for the backstretch. The key was a decision by Meeker, a former Marine Corps officer who had served three tours in Vietnam, and who was certainly no knee-knocking bleeding heart. Meeker had begun an employee assistance program (EAP) to serve Churchill's own employees, mainly the track's frontside workers, in 1987. The EAP was, of course, a way to help troubled employees and their families, but it was also viewed as a way to increase productivity and profitability.

"The problem extends beyond alcohol, beyond drug abuse," Meeker said at the 1990 Conference on Alcohol and Drug Abuse Programs for the Horse Racing Industry. "It extends right down to the fabric of our industry, and some of the things that we found that were happening in the industry demonstrated proof positive to us that we had to do something. Some of the things that we saw were an escalation of our insurance rates, absenteeism creeping into the company where we were losing time. We were losing the investment in experience and education that we had invested in individuals in our company; and all in all, we were not getting a full day's work out of many of our employees."

Meeker also noted in his presentation that he too had undergone treatment for alcoholism in 1989. "There's a commitment on our part to make sure that we, one, identify individuals who are suffering from the disease; two, provide them an opportunity for self-help; and three, to the extent that is necessary, we'll provide them the means to seek treatment and to attempt to arrest their disease at some point in the future, hopefully. Why do we do it? We do it for the same reason that anyone who's in business wants to do it. We want higher productivity. We want a safer workplace, and we want to make sure that the individuals that we have working for us are good, solid, loyal, dedicated, and experienced individuals," he said. "And we do it quite honestly for a self-serving purpose, and that is to improve our business."

With a frontside EAP in place, McDonald took the opportunity to suggest a similar program for the backstretch. It would be a unique program, however, in at least two ways. First, it would be a rigorous and structured program, drawing on state-of-the- art expertise rather than the sort of bootstrap effort so common in horse racing's efforts. Second, it would be paid for by management, as a management initiative on the backstretch. What evolved by July 1, 1989, was the Lifestyle Program of Churchill Downs, whose genesis will be described in greater detail below.

Once they had decided to act, Meeker and McDonald pursued creation of the Churchill program in conjunction with the University of Louisville's newly created Department of Equine Administration, headed by Dr. Robert G. Lawrence, and with U of L's Norton Psychiatric Clinic, a part of Alliant Health System. Alliant Health system provided Churchill's frontside EAP program, so the connection was a natural. The connection with a co-author was a natural as well. Paul McDonald and Dr. Curtis Barrett had served in the Naval Reserve together for some 20 years.

It was clear, from the outset, that the program had the support of Warner Jones. Jones did not talk about the Lifestyle Program; he called it the "backside AA program." Although he had not put AA formally into his recovery program initially, Jones recognized that not everybody would have a chance to recover in the way he did. Jones's method of helping was to go over to a closed bookshelf, open it, and show a whole row of Vernon Johnson's book, *I'll Quit Tomorrow.* He would pull one out, endorse it, and use his own example to show what recovery could do. One of the co-authors has a copy of Johnson's book, duly endorsed by Warner Jones.

Churchill's chairman truly wanted the recovery program to be available on the race track, to an industry that he loved and served in his own way. The company he headed had embarked on a new path, not out of sentimentality, but out of commitment. He had looked for and found the opportunity to help horse people. Indeed, none who saw him stand outside of the Lifestyle Program office, on the backstretch of Churchill Downs, joining hands with fellow alcoholics and saying the Lord's Prayer, will ever forget his example. But those who felt Warner Jones's size 12 shoe on their behinds, along with a ticket to treatment in Minnesota, are not likely to forget the forceful side of Jones, either.

From their limited perspective, those associated with the nascent Churchill program believed they were in uncharted waters in creating a backstretch program to treat addictions. Bob Lawrence, however, knew that they were not. He had come to the University of Louisville from Maryland, where a race track program had been launched under a contract with the University of Maryland. Dr. Lawrence suggested contacts with Bob Babes, who had pioneered Maryland's Horsemen's Counseling Program, and that contact led to Jim Ryan. In time, those contacts would involve Churchill's Lifestyle Program in Ryan's plan for financial support to establish 54 on-track addiction programs and to the first Conference on Alcohol and Drug Abuse Programs for the Horse Racing Industry in 1989.

In December 1988, Meeker approved a proposal from the University of Louisville and the Norton Psychiatric Clinic for a backstretch program at Churchill Downs that would be financed by the track and would represent a management initiative to provide a service that, at that time, was not being performed by any other entity. Meeker said he wanted a program of excellence, a program that would provide for on-track counseling, and one that might serve as a model for other on-track programs in Kentucky and throughout the industry. While clearly committing Churchill to creating a program, Meeker said he believed the effort should extend to all Kentucky tracks to provide for continuity of treatment. He correctly perceived that an individual should be able to go to any track, receive treatment for alcoholism or other addiction, and then move to a similar program at the next track.

Rather than seeking to reinvent the wheel, the designers of the Lifestyle Program modeled it on the successful United States Navy multilevel initiative against alcohol and drug abuse. Just as the Navy's program had to be aboard ship, it was imperative that the race track program be on the race track, staffed by persons who were familiar with the environment and its protocols. The Navy model and the Churchill program had four elements reflecting levels of training: volunteers, an on-track peer acting as liaison between racetrack workers and treatment professionals, masters-level counselors, and a doctoral-level adviser for back-up.

The first element was called the volunteer assistance group. Going into a new environment, the program's creators needed to find out what the race track itself was already doing to deal with the problem, to see where the role models were, and to see where people naturally turned for help.

In doing that, the Churchill program initiators were following the scientific literature from psychotherapy and, especially, the work of Hans Strupp at Vanderbilt University. Dr. Strupp had identified a group in the university environment to whom students frequently turned in time of trouble, and he labeled them the inherently helping persons. When students had problems, they would go to these inherently helping people instead of going to the counseling center, if they had one available. Churchill's program, therefore, was to be anchored in the volunteer assistance group, or the inherently helping people of the track. Among these volunteers would be persons involved in 12-step programs, industry leaders such as Warner Jones, and some enlightened trainers. Ideally, volunteers would have solid personal recovery from alcoholism or other addiction.

The next element, or level, was the on-track liaison, which was viewed as the linchpin of the entire program. The position required a person who knew both the race track and the problems of alcohol and drug abuse. In concept, this individual was given an unfortunate tag name – "bird dog" – that caused enormous problems to be explained later. However, the individual who was selected for this key position had all of the prerequisites.

With just a few months on the job, Bill Chenault explained his role at the first Louisville Conference in 1989. After returning from World War II and attending the University of Louisville at night for a while, "I went through my period of testing old John Barleycorn," he said. "For many years, I bought race horses. I've had the privilege of enjoying the winner's circle on occasion at the tracks in Arkansas and down in Louisiana and down in Florida and up in the East in Pennsylvania, Monmouth, and Atlantic City. I do know something about losing, and one time I applied for a job after I had gotten rid of my race horses, and they almost got rid of me, to tell you the truth. They are very expensive things. But anyhow, I applied for this job and this counselor said: 'Mr. Chenault, what did you do?' I said: 'Well, I owned race horses.' He said: 'What did you like most about your job?' I said: 'Winning.' He said: 'What did you like the least?' I said: 'Losing.' That was the way it was. I didn't get the job. But the most important thing, and what I want to make clear, is that I enjoy being where I am. I am on the backside rather than the frontside, and I think I can get along back there. I do believe that what does not come from the heart does not reach the heart."

A racetracker himself, Chenault understood the racetracker. "Now, the most important thing for me to keep in mind is that each one of these folks on the backside is an individual who has their likes and dislikes, just like I do. There is a fierce loyalty that I've found on the backside. They believe in winning, but they can also lose with a certain amount of dignity. They have to have that, or it will destroy them. They give a tremendous attachment to a horse. I'm talking about the grooms. The trainers, of course, but the grooms and the hotwalkers, and they follow that horse, and they fall in love with that horse, if you will. That's my experience with watching them and listening to them. When that horse wins, it's an experience for them, it's like a high, and they have a good time. What else are they going to have? They can watch the football games and the baseball games and things of that nature on television. But these people get up 5 o'clock, 4:30 in the morning, and they have their hours that are different than the people on the outside. So the pleasures, it seems to me, that appeal to them don't necessarily appeal to everybody else. Also, their place belongs to them, and I never want to invade that dignity with any sort of pompous attitude that I can cure them or anything like that," Chenault said. "I'm on a level with them one day at a time. I want them to feel comfortable when they come to see me, and when they leave I want them to feel like they can come back."

Four years later, Chenault said that he had no need to go looking for clients. "I don't trace them down. They come to me," he said at the 1993 Louisville Conference. "I try to talk to them about the horse, which they love, and about the job, which they depend upon, and about eventually the problem they suffer from. But it's a three-stage process with me individually. I don't say this will work for everybody. I'm telling you what works for me."

As the person charged with liaison work, Chenault also sought to establish contacts with the trainers, who employ the backstretch workers. "I must say that it takes time to make contact with trainers who wish to do something, and they have to make a living, too, and they have to look at their side of it. I don't go into their shedrow. I'm invited into their shedrow. I stand outside of their shedrow; and when I'm invited in to talk to them, I come in. I don't force myself on any of them. I don't have any absolute power. I believe, to use an old cliche, absolute power corrupts completely and absolutely. The power which works with suffering, addictive people comes in a one-to-one basis when I can get in contact with them and to hear some of the truths that finally comes through as to where they are; and that's what we work on at Churchill Downs."

The third level of Churchill's program, in terms of professional education if not life experience, calls for a counselor, formally trained at the master's level. This individual is not required to be knowledgeable about the race track but must be willing to learn about it. Credentials and professional experience come first in this position. In addition to knowledge of addictive disorders, and their treatment, training in psychopathology, substance abuse, and personality theory, are required. State Certification as a chemical dependency counselor, which became available in Kentucky, is highly desirable. The individual in this position schedules to be on the race track between eight and 12 hours a week – depending on the racing season – and deals with not only the addiction problems but also the lifestyle problems that are presented.

The final element, or level, for the model is at the doctoral-level and calls for a psychiatrist or clinical psychologist. In the case of the Lifestyle Program, this individual is also the director of the program. The specific role of the person in this position, called for by the model, is bringing to bear more intensive psychotherapy based on a broader level of training, knowledge, and experience. Family or employer intervention and Cognitive Behavioral Therapy are examples of such services. Also, the doctoral level person is responsible for liaison efforts in the community so that resources are kept available to the racetrackers who need them. All too often, clients from the race track do not receive adequate treatment in the community because their lifestyle is not understood by the treating professional. Doctor to doctor communication often solves that problem. Finally, having a doctoral level staff member helps to assure that problems that need to be treated in a medical setting, or even in a hospital, will be referred there.

While Churchill was able to commit to providing an on-track Lifestyle Program, the corporation certainly could not provide hospital care for race track personnel who needed such treatment. The cost of such service obviously would be far greater if the program expanded and a statewide network of programs was established. Initially, it appeared that hospitalization and other medical care might be provided to licensees through the Kentucky Racing Health and Welfare Fund. This entity functions under the supervision of the Kentucky Racing Commission and is supported by escheat checks, i.e., the winning parimutuel tickets that are not cashed by those who hold them. Kentucky is exceptional in dedicating these funds to indigent licensees, for medical care, instead of putting them into the general fund or providing them for non-racing worthy causes, e.g., mental retardation. This source of payment for in-patient care proved to be unavailable for addicted licensees, especially those with additional mental illness.

Following through on his view that what Churchill was establishing could be a good model for other Kentucky race tracks, Tom Meeker convened a meeting of the state's racing interests at the Aristides Room of the Kentucky Derby Museum on January 10, 1989.

Representatives of race tracks, the racing commission, horsemen's organizations, security personnel, the Health and Welfare Fund, the University of Louisville, Alliant Health System, and others were in attendance. At that time, Meeker proposed two programs. The first was an industry-wide program similar to the one that Churchill Downs was establishing, that would deal with alcoholism and other addictive disorders on Kentucky s race tracks. The second program he called "Doc in a Box." The idea was to equip a trailer as a mobile medical clinic, properly staffed, and move it from track to track as racing meets moved. Meeker announced that Churchill Downs was putting up $50,000 for initial funding of its Lifestyle Program and to match an expected $20,000 from the Ryan Family Foundation. He asked other tracks to commit, at least, to matching Ryan Family Foundation grants, and establish an on-track Lifestyle Program. On the spot, Turfway Park agreed to do so and Ellis Park, not represented at the meeting, came on board later.

The reception of the Churchill Downs proposal was, at best, lukewarm. This was something of a surprise, and it signaled other troubles to come. While some mistakes were made in providing information for the proposal, especially in the area of program costs, it became clear that other factors were involved in the lukewarm reception. A hint came in one comment after the meeting: "I don't see why (name of track) should have anything to do with a program based in Louisville." It seemed that Kentucky's traditional regionalism, and difficulties with statewide cooperation, were at work against the proposal.

Hindsight suggests that another factor, peculiar to horse racing, was at work at well. The Lifestyle Program was presented as a management initiative, benefitting those who work on the backstretch but are not employed by the association, and it was going to be administered by the frontside. Without doubt, this played into traditional turf issues and triggered competition, not cooperation.

What happened thereafter is ironic. While the Kentucky Racing Health and Welfare Fund and the horsemen's organizations previously had eschewed coverage of treatment for addicted licensees after some costly treatment failures, they now began a concerted effort to create an alternative to the Churchill Downs proposal. The guiding principle seemed to be, as one of those who was working to find an alternative put it, "what we create, we support." Because management had proposed the Lifestyle Program, it was all but certain that some groups would not support it. For other groups, the focus was on developing a less expensive approach.

Licensees who formerly had been rejected outright when they applied for help with their addiction became the targets of the new, competitive program. One pundit termed this, with a play on the Kentucky Derby's Run for the Roses, as the "Run for the Addicts."

The Thoroughbred Addictions Council of Kentucky was formed and became the vehicle for the first alternative to the Lifestyle Program. This program differed significantly from the Lifestyle Program in its manner of funding, its philosophy of dealing with troubled licensees, and its staffing. Also, there was a concerted but unsuccessful effort to make programs of the Thoroughbred Addictions Council of Kentucky the only option available to licensees who found themselves in trouble by having it designated as the Racing Commission's official program. With the failure of that effort, two programs were at work at Turfway, Ellis, and Churchill. Keeneland Race Course developed a chaplaincy-based program that, after about a year, merged with the Thoroughbred Addictions Council of Kentucky.

There seem to be two important lessons to be gained from this part of the Kentucky experience. First, the years have shown there to be some benefit in having more than one option available to licensees and to race track stewards and security. One of the authors, as consultant to the Association of Racing Commissioners International's Uniform Rules Committee, strongly recommended that racing commissions not select a single program and require licensees to use it. Licensees are responsible for the success of the program they receive and, therefore, should have a choice. Second, outsiders who enter the world of horse racing, with a new idea or program, should be aware of the industry's capacity to absorb, obstruct, and outlast programs and ideas that threaten to upset its equilibrium.

Those who proposed the Lifestyle Program made some tactical mistakes. The first error was using a term – "bird dog" – that had a positive meaning outside of racing and a very negative meaning on the backstretch. This term was used to describe one of the roles of the on-track liaison person, namely, that of finding and identifying persons who need help. On the race track, it was quickly pointed out, a bird dog is a snitch, a despicable individual who cannot be trusted and turns in fellow racetrackers to the stewards or the police. Experienced race track personnel, beginning at the meeting called by Meeker, were incensed at the idea of management establishing a backstretch snitch or bird dog.

The second tactical error involved money, or financial estimates. Meeker told the group that Churchill was adding $50,000 to the $20,000 matching grant from the Ryan Family Foundation for establishing a program. Partly because cost estimates were assembled hastily and were based on a less than thorough knowledge of backstretch arrangements and the ultimate structure of the Lifestyle Program, the initial cost estimates were very high. This raised fears that the tracks and the Health and Welfare Fund, and possibly horsemen's groups, might ultimately shoulder the cost of a very expensive program. Another factor in the high cost figures, which in retrospect deserve no apology, is that the estimate was based on serving all of Kentucky's horse industry. At the time, Kentucky had two racing commissions. One served the Thoroughbred industry. The other served the Standardbred, Quarter Horse, Arabian, and other breeds of racing. Since those present at Meeker's meeting were all from the Thoroughbred side of Kentucky racing, there certainly was no interest in developing a program to serve the other breeds. Today, Kentucky has one racing commission that is charged with serving all of the Commonwealth's horse racing interests.

One of the co-authors served as the doctoral level director of the Lifestyle Programs established by Churchill Downs, Turfway Park, and Ellis Park. John Mullins, a Navy-trained counselor who let his personal experiences with alcoholism be known early in most relationships, served Turfway Park and Ellis Park in the way that Bill Chenault, and others, have served Churchill Downs as the on-track liaison person. Although not previously associated with horse racing, Mullins had outstanding success in bringing the Alcoholics Anonymous influence to the race track. John Mullins left the racing industry and its addictive-disorders programs after four years to return to a private-sector counseling role. Management changes, for the most part, resulted in less interest in a management initiative to deal with addictions problems on the backstretch of the tracks where Mullins had worked, and they folded.

The Lifestyle Program at Churchill Downs has continued to function successfully and maintains a full caseload. The program has been successful in reaching some individuals before they have been in trouble with the racing commission or racetrack security. Of course, some of the program's clients are referred by regulators or security and, in such cases, the program works with these authorities and assists licensees in complying with rulings. The program has not had good success in reaching women and Hispanics. Certainly, this has not been for want of trying to attract clients from these underserved groups. Similarly, a goal of the Lifestyle Program has been to establish a drug-free workplace. So far, that has not met with success.

Among race track programs, Churchill's Lifestyle Program has several unique characteristics. The starting place is the program's name. Mark Wilson, then Churchill's general counsel and management's coordinator of the Lifestyle Program, saw that the program would deal both with alcoholism and drug addiction as primary diseases and with alcohol and drug abuse as symptoms of lifestyle problems. While even some professionals will debate the distinction between addiction and abuse, the idea that some individuals have to use drugs (addiction) while others choose to use drugs as a way of coping (abuse) has considerable appeal. In the extremely competitive race track environment, in particular, admitting to a fault is very difficult to do. Counselors may well lose the opportunity to help at all by browbeating an individual who suggests that there are reasonable explanations for his or her drug or alcohol use. The term lifestyle problem encompasses both psychopathology, or mental disorders including addiction, and the problems and conflicts that normal people encounter in the course of living. The Lifestyle Program takes the position that any problem affecting safety or productivity on the race track is worth correcting. Marital or relationship problems, living with a chronic illness or injury, vocational and educational choices, child rearing problems, correcting a criminal record, finding medical care for a loved one, and many other problems have been moved toward solution by

Lifestyle Program counselors. Usually, alcohol and drugs played a part somewhere in the pattern, but were not of first priority. Wilson, as it turns out, was correct in naming Churchill's initiative the Lifestyle Program.

Second, the Lifestyle Program practiced prevention in a way that works on the backstretch. Simply put, prevention means being there. It means having a visible presence so that individuals come in and get to know about the program well before they, or someone they know, has a need. The Lifestyle Program's office is right on the major traffic pattern of the backstretch. Walking by, and looking into the office, one usually sees a few racetrackers in the office, having a cup of coffee, and talking. There is a friendly atmosphere and all are welcome. Signs and literature communicate what the office is there for, but there is no pressure. The posture taken by the professional staff is that proven in scientific literature to be most helpful: the friendly teacher. This same attitude is taken to the shedrow as counselors make their daily rounds. Friendly. Teacher. Alcoholics Anonymous would call it the principle of attraction.

Finally, the Lifestyle Program is moving toward addressing addictions that do not involve ingestion of a chemical. The best example, of course, is problem or pathological gambling, a devastating disorder that is increasing in the general population. It is increasing among racing industry personnel. The worst aspect of pathological gambling is that it remains hidden until the addiction has progressed to a very serious stage. Gamblers don't smell, stagger, or have slurred speech. The Lifestyle Program has been advised by some to steer clear of a problem that is based in use of the very product that racing provides: gambling. However, Churchill Downs management has taken the opposite view, and the Lifestyle Program has been ready to follow the lead. That is, pathological gambling needs to be prevented, if possible, and dealt with competently when prevention fails.

In Kentucky, as in some other states, the Standardbred industry has been "missing in action" with regard to programs dealing with lifestyle, alcoholism, and drug addiction. For a while, it appeared that the leadership of Wayne Shumate, chairman of the Kentucky Harness Racing Commission and president of the Association of Racing Commissioners International, would assure the Standardbred industry's participation. However, that did not happen. Three possible factors account for this. First, the Standardbred industry generally regards itself as a family-oriented industry and believes that it has a smaller problem with chemical dependency than Thoroughbred racing. Second, harness racing drivers have long been required to take a Breathalyzer test prior to a day's racing and remain in a monitored space until the end of their race day. This is cited as attention enough. Third, the Standardbred industry in Kentucky has been in retreat during the period in which the Lifestyle Program was established, and survival has had priority.

The Old Kentucky Home experience has had more success in spreading its effects to the nonracing components of Kentucky's horse industry. Efforts of the Lifestyle Program and the University of Louisville Equine Administration Program to attract the attention of the Saddlebred industry have proved successful. Presentations have been made to Saddlebred organizations, such as the United Professional Horsemen's Association and the American Equestrian Medical Association, by one of the authors. On one occasion, Hall of Fame jockey Pat Day was featured in a presentation. The most tangible result has been establishing a nonalcoholic hospitality suite at the World's Championship Horse Show held each year in Louisville. A member of the Lifestyle Program staff, Camille Frey, and prominent Saddlebred owner Jim Cooke persuaded those in charge of the horse show, Joseph Stopher and William Munford, of the need, and they responded enthusiastically. Although the event lasts only one week, the attitude and procedures used by the Lifestyle Program of Churchill Downs work quite well with troubled individuals from the Saddlebred show.

Warner L. Jones Jr., who sincerely wanted to help the suffering racetracker, died in early 1994, but the work that he supported goes on and is expanding. The Lifestyle Program stands as a tribute to his leadership and concern as well as to the vision of Tom Meeker, who provided the initial call for excellence and then faced down those who wanted a less comprehensive program. Paul McDonald Jr. received the Jefferson Cup – the highest honor of Jefferson County, which includes Louisville – in 1989 for his work in bringing help and hope to the backstretch of Churchill Downs. He had not forgotten or forsaken his old Kentucky home.

Chapter 10

The Whole Person

Lucy Reum was a pioneer and a radical innovator in a highly conservative sport. In the male-dominated world of horse racing, she made a difference in Illinois. Through her efforts – first as a member of the Illinois Racing Board, then as its chairperson in 1976 and 1977, and as the founder of the Racing Industry Charitable Foundation – she helped to create the first comprehensive program of services for the backstretch worker. She undertook this estimable but daunting task for two reasons: first, she looked upon her appointment to the Racing Board as a public trust and responsibility; and second, she cared about the conditions on Illinois's race tracks. She was not one of those racing commissioners who look at deplorable living and working conditions and say, "Well, it's not my job." Lucy Reum (pronounced Reem) saw it as part of her public trust to ensure satisfactory conditions for all of the state's residents – even those living and working on the race track. From the effort that she set in motion, Illinois has developed the most comprehensive system of backstretch services – services that address the whole person.

"Mrs. Reum, who had never really had much to do with the racing industry until she was appointed by the governor, went to the backstretch, and she was absolutely appalled," said Peggy Goetsch, executive director of the Illinois Racing Industry Charitable Foundation. "She proceeded to write a report making recommendations to the Illinois Racing Board, recommending that on-site medical, dental, and social services be provided, at least to the Chicago-area Thoroughbred community," said Goetsch, who has been associated with the foundation since 1982. "As part of the Racing Board, she initiated changes which drastically improved housing at all of the race tracks and the conditions for these horsemen." Housing, Reum concluded, was not the whole answer. In looking at the race track environment, she observed that "that this is a very isolated community with very little resources, very migratory in nature; and they did not have access to medical services or dental services because of their schedules, because of lack of money, and really because of the reluctance of the community surrounding the race tracks to take care of these people," Goetsch said. After Reum's term on the Racing Board expired in 1977, she formed the Racing Industry Charitable Foundation, composed of leading figures in the racing industry and the community. "Their first task was to raise money to provide these on-site medical, dental, and social services, and also add day-care services to it. Usually, they sought first-time grants from some local charities. As they went along, they used their own influences with the industry to persuade the Illinois Racing Board to allocate a certain number of charity days to them to provide more consistency in funding," Goetsch said at the 1989 Conference on Alcohol and Drug Abuse Programs for the Horse Racing Industry.

With the funds, medical, dental, social services, and child-care services were initiated at the Chicago Thoroughbred tracks and, to a lesser extent at the city's Standardbred tracks. The charity days, in which proceeds from specific racing days were allocated to charitable purposes, turned out to be less than consistent. If the weather turned cold or rainy, the charity was the big loser. "I remember one meet we lost $82,000," Goetsch said. "The charity-day system was very difficult. We lived through it for nine years, and actually services were not of the highest quality. We really limped along, never really able to develop new programs because we were at the mercy of the charity days, the weather, the track you were assigned. It was feast or famine."

In 1988, as Illinois's race tracks were entering the world of off-track betting, "our organization, working along with the race track operators and Illinois Racing Board, encouraged the Illinois General Assembly to do away with the charity-day system. Instead, we wanted to have mandated contributions from the race track to go to the Illinois Racing Board and be disseminated that way. That was passed in 1988 and went into effect in 1989," Goetsch said. The track owners effectively capped their expenses for backstretch human services, a strategy that became a problem for the foundation's programs in the mid-1990s. Compared with earlier years, though, the foundation had stumbled upon a pot of money. "In 1989, out of the $750,000 that was available, we were awarded $525,000, which was an increase of about 300 percent in our revenues. With the tremendous increase that we received, we were mandated to do these programs at all of our race tracks, not just the Chicago-area race tracks. In addition, we were mandated to begin an outpatient, on-site addiction treatment services at our race tracks," said Goetsch, who put together the enlarged Illinois system over three months. The program was extended to seven Illinois race tracks – reduced to six in the 1990s with the closing of Quad City Downs harness track.

"The challenge really began then, and the biggest challenge was really initially not only to put together a very competent group of professionals very quickly and get them acclimated to the backstretch and to the racing industry, but the biggest challenge was really getting the racing industry to accept some of these programs. So what we did was we began by developing a board of directors that was representative of top managers in the racing industry of the tracks, track owners, trainers, owners of horses, jockeys, harness drivers and representatives of all of our industry. And we were very successful in doing that," Goetsch said at the 1989 Louisville Conference. "We have a board of 25 people, and it's rather crazy sometimes; but it really has helped to first work with these people and educate them and have that trickle down, and that has been very successful. Given the various facets of the industry that are represented at some of our board meetings, there are times that we feel that we should get a Nobel Peace Prize for bringing some of these people together. But it has worked well."

In addition, Goetsch and the board had to help a new group of professionals to adapt to the racing industry. "It was a much different situation than most of these professionals had encountered. Instead of sitting in their offices waiting for clients to come to them, these professionals went out into the stable areas with boots on and all of that and really got to know their clientele and tried to establish some trust there."

Step by step, the program has grown and developed. In 1994, the foundation's program had a peak payroll of 38, including six addictions counselors. At the Chicago-area Thoroughbred tracks alone in 1993, the program had 13,000 medical contacts. "We're providing the family doctor to the backstretch personnel," Goetsch said. "We're very involved in public-health issues on the backstretch as well. We're providing dental clinics on-site. We've increased those every year."

In providing the services, the foundation's staff and executive director have made some significant discoveries about the backstretch community. "The unique thing about the industry is that many of them do not want to move out of the industry," Goetsch said. "They become part of that racing subculture and do not want to go beyond the gates." For immigrant groups, the backstretch is less stressful than more complex portions of American business and society. They can, for instance, function in their native language, and they have co-workers who also use that language exclusively. Moreover, some members of this immigrant population come from rural areas, and their skills are best suited to husbandry. "There's a love for the animal," Goetsch said.

She said the foundation's workers also have found that they often must go into the community, rather than having community members come to them for services. "We're beginning to use outreach as a method of case management, which is very effective with some of the subcultures on track and with women. You have to keep at it and keep at it, which is contrary to what I learned in school, that you wait until the client comes to you," she said. "We're trying to empower our patients and our clients. The focus is on empowering the client. Medically for some of these people, it's strange to focus on yourself and on your own health. It was unheard of for many people. We're trying to build that 'You are important.' The horses are important here, but the human beings are the most important. We try to empower them to take control of their own lives."

The Illinois program also has a responsibility that other track-based providers do not: children. "We have a unique situation in Illinois – children on the backstretch. At some of our Thoroughbred tracks, we have 350 children. So that certainly changes our focus a great deal," Goetsch said. "It's very difficult tracking down new children that come on the track, and we're very concerned about immunization and about educating the parents. And, we're concerned about their safety." The program also has increased its services to women, including mammography on track.

Representing a wide range of professionals and specialties, the Illinois foundation's staff can apply a holistic approach to substance abuse and addiction. "Each case is looked at individually," Goetsch said, and the professionals bring their viewpoints to the table. "When you get multiple disciplines together, there are differences of opinion, but I think that's healthy," she said.

The substance-abuse program, which has been licensed by the state since 1989, offers both treatment and counseling, both essentially in programs of at least six months. Counseling often includes cases of driving under the influence of alcohol, and it is utilized for those clients who are abusing drugs but are not addicted. Goetsch said that, in appropriate cases, on-track treatment has been successful. "We find that you can treat them on-track, and sometimes it is very effective. They'll usually come into treatment after we've put them in a three- to five-day detox. They can't come in using, obviously," she said. "Some people that we've seen over and over are not going to make it in an outpatient setting. There are too many triggers on the backstretch, and it's not going to work. We try to move them into inpatient treatment, or even outpatient treatment off-track."

The on-track regimen involves, after detoxification, an intense eight weeks of treatment. "They are doing four groups a week, and individual counseling once or twice a week," Goetsch said. "We begin to introduce them to the 12-step concepts, so they're very busy in the first eight weeks. The rest of the time is aftercare, and they continue with one or two groups a week. They're in counseling to deal with their alcohol and drug problems and, if need be, in psychological counseling as well." The foundation program also has helped to establish meetings of Alcoholics Anonymous, Narcotics Anonymous, and Gamblers Anonymous at the tracks.

The program also moved early to get itself into the backstretch community, through personal contacts, posters, and 800 numbers. The tactics resulted in a shift in the proportions of mandated and voluntary clients. "It's kind of interesting that since we have become a licensed outpatient program, we're now getting about 40 percent of our referrals from the stewards," Goetsch said at the 1990 Louisville Conference. "That was about 70 percent, but right now that's about 40 percent. Sixty percent is voluntary participation now, which means that our counselors and our staff are getting out there and really getting the message out."

Getting the message out and providing the services costs money, and the 1988 legislation put a lid on the tracks' costs without making any provision for inflation. The $750,000 annual allocation continued into the mid-1990s without an increase. "To this point, it has worked pretty well because it is a consistent income and something we weren't used to. But it's capped, and costs increase, particularly when you're offering health services. For me, the annual increases in health costs have been around 12 percent or higher," Goetsch said in 1994. "I have a five-year plan so that we can continue to operate. This year, we're budgeted at $823,000, so that additional money has to come from somewhere. So I think we're very conservative in our spending. We have some small reserves, and I constantly have to look at fund development, whether in fund raising or grants or whatever. The only private source of funds that we have had is Jim Ryan, and that helped tremendously. We haven't looked at private funds yet, but that's something we absolutely have to look at."

Money is one of the concerns that Goetsch must address. Another is awareness of substance abuse itself. Goetsch said she discovered that not every member of the board fully understands the depth of the substance-abuse problem on the backstretch. In 1993, Goetsch said, "a director said, 'Well, have we taken care of the drug problem on the backstretch?' He wanted me to say, 'Yes, it's marvelous.' But I said it's terrible. It's worse than ever. This guy got so angry. He said we're not doing anything. But then I started to talk to them about how that is something every member of the board of directors should take some responsibility for. They listened. I guess we're moving forward."

Sometimes, though, the progress is imperceptible. Goetsch said she listened once while a trainer complained angrily about his high level of workers' compensation claims and about his soaring insurance costs. "Then I walked into his tack room, and his assistant trainer and two grooms are smoking a joint. He smelled it; he knew what was going on. It just knocks you over. This is a bright guy."

She conceded that the trainers have been difficult to work with, but she would like to work with them and develop educational programs for them. "I'd like to see a drug-free workplace in the backstretch of the race track. I'd like to teach trainers that, yes, you should expect your employees not to be impaired on the job. I think you have to educate on the management level of the track and even with the regulators. I'm doing that now, but it's a slow process."

Sometimes, examples speak louder than words, and Goetsch pointed to the example of a foundation board member, the late Ernie Poulos, a successful Chicago-area horseman who trained Black Tie Affair, the 1991 Horse of the Year. "If you look at some of the more successful stables, such as Ernie Poulos's, they're clean and the workers don't appear to be impaired. It just works like clockwork, and they're the ones that win the big races and the big money. You can feel a sense of professionalism and pride in there," she said. "We have a lot of things to work through, but I have seen a lot of good things happen. But they happen slowly." Caring for the whole person never has happened in a hurry.

Chapter 11

The Cop and the Jock

They were as dissimilar as two people could ever be, the cop and the jock. The cop was a rock-solid veteran who had seen just about everything of life's underbelly in his 21 years on New York City's mean streets. He was a product of the city, and the accent of his voice was as distinctive as the Empire State Building's silhouette. The jock was young, brash, engaging. "Designer shades and good-looking women," was how his former long-time agent described him. The jock had emerged from the country of South Carolina, and he seemed forever in awe of the world's wonders and the various urban delights. He also was a natural in the saddle, and he had taken the East Coast by storm, moving from success in Maryland to success in New Jersey to success in New York – the Big Apple, The Show, the racing circuit where most riders yearn to be. In 1988, he would ride the favorite in the Kentucky Derby.

That year in New York, the paths of Dominick Bologna, the former New York City narcotics and homicide cop, and leading jockey Chris Antley would cross. Antley had become mixed up with drugs, and Bologna was the man at the New York State Racing and Wagering Board who dealt with drug offenders on the race track. In different hands or with a different approach and philosophy, this could have been yet another race track tragedy: jock gets rich and famous; jock messes up three times; jock loses his career. But, in large part because of Dominick Bologna's compassionate approach to the substance abuser (but not the drug abuse), Chris Antley returned to the race track and went on to greater accomplishments. In 1991, Antley guided Strike the Gold to a late-charging victory in the Kentucky Derby. A life

– and a career – had been saved.

THE COP

When Chris Antley was born on January 6, 1966, Dom Bologna had already logged several years as a uniformed policeman on the New York City force. That year is regarded by some observers as the beginning of monumental change in American society – a social revolution whose history was marked most visibly by the nation's divisions over the Vietnam war and the much-publicized generation gap. To be sure, the generation that grew up after World War II was much different from the one that had survived Depression and world conflict. Youth rebelled against its elders, and the drug culture spread from America's poorest neighborhoods and infected the college campuses and middle-class suburbia. In a period of unsettling changes, the government responded to a perceived problem – drugs on Main Street – by throwing money at the problem. Dom Bologna was one of the beneficiaries of America's first war on drugs. "Any time they had a problem in this area, their response was to let the police handle it. Let's throw more money at it. Let's create more narcotics detectives," said Bologna, who moved out of uniform in 1969. "I was a young uniformed guy trying to get promoted, and I started to work at that time in plainclothes operations. Before I know it, I got transferred into the detective division as a narcotics detective. I spent two years doing that, and from there I went into homicide, and I spent my remaining years on the police department there," said Bologna, who retired in 1982 after more than two decades of service.

When he first became a narc, Bologna started with a law enforcer's stereotypical view of the drug abuser or addict. "As a policeman, I didn't think much of people who used drugs. I thought they were subhuman," he said. "At the end of two years, working with informers, I didn't understand why they used drugs, but I realized they weren't as bad as I thought they were. That's when I started to dislike what I was doing in narcotics, and I was happy to leave there, because I saw the destruction it wreaked upon the individual and the family."

When he retired, Bologna went to work as an investigator for the New York State Racing and Wagering Board, the state's official overseer of Thoroughbred and Standardbred racing. The board's chairman then was John Van Lindt, who had been a Manhattan homicide prosecutor when Bologna was a homicide detective. Van Lindt also remembered that Bologna had spent a tour of duty in narcotics. "He says, 'Dominick, weren't you a narc? Weren't you a narcotics detective?' I said: 'Yeah, why?' He said: 'Well, I want to establish a drug-abuse program. I want to test jockeys and make sure that we protect the life and the property on the track and maintain the integrity of racing. I think that's why we're all here anyway, among other things.' I said: 'But John, I don't know anything about drug abuse. I know how to make arrests.' He said: 'Well, I don't want you to do that. I want you to do a little research and see what you can come up with, and present it to me in two weeks.' "

Bologna, who presented the genesis of the New York program at the 1989 Conference on Alcohol and Drug Abuse Program for the Horse Racing Industry, said he sought help from the New York Division of Substance Abuse Services, and he received a fast but thorough education. "I started to get some training from the state Division of Substance Abuse Services as to what drug use was all about and what addiction was. I started to get a different perspective on drugs than I had as a policeman. The only thing I knew about drugs as a policeman was how to make an arrest. Then I started to understand. I started to learn what addiction was all about and what drugs do. I got trained by those people," he said. "The courses I've taken with the people at the Division of Substance Abuse Services taught me why certain people are prone to have a relationship with these dangerous substances. They are the ones who really turn you around when it comes to understanding what a druggie is." On his own time, Bologna took further courses, "mainly for my own edification."

In the end, Bologna's edification contributed to a professional, sophisticated program. It would not, for instance, be a drug agency. It was the Stress Assistance Program."We call it that because, from the very beginning, I was advised that people use drugs because of an inability to handle stress in their lives," he said. He emphasized that he is not a care provider; rather, he is a care facilitator. "I haven't cured anybody in my years here. I'm not a counselor, although I consider myself a student of the problem of alcohol and drug abuse," he said. "I think we have a positive program. Our mission is not to punish people or to knock people out of racing. Our mission is to protect the people on the track from those who might be using illegal drugs and to help those who are having a problem to get their lives back on track and under control, and to get them working again."

Undoubtedly, jockeys and drivers have plenty of stress in their lives, but so do trainers, and starters, and anyone whose life goes out of control. Although Van Lindt originally wanted the testing program for the sports' most visible players – the jocks and the drivers – Bologna argued successfully that the program should apply to every one of the 40,000 people with a license from the New York racing board, which means everyone from the chairman of the New York Racing Association to the newest hotwalker. "At the time, some of our attorneys were advising that we should only test jockeys and harness drivers. I said, 'Wait, why should we single these people out?'," Bologna said. "Trainers, starters, grooms, and valets also have to do with the safety on the track. We like to talk about integrity in this business. Even if you are an owner or an exercise rider or whatever, if you're using drugs doesn't that breach our integrity?" Clearly, the answer was yes.

Bologna also helped to shape the racing board's testing policies. When he first started to devise a testing policy, he recognized that drug testing was not as widely accepted as it would be in the 1990s. "The attitude of the New York State Racing and Wagering Board is such that asking an individual to submit to a test is an invasion of one's privacy, and it's ingrained in our culture that we get rid of our body fluids in private and we don't hold it up to inspection," Bologna said in 1989. "But in achieving the safety of our people on the track, the protection of the property they come in contact with, and the integrity of the game, we feel that this rule is necessary to achieve those objectives. So we have a policy of testing; we have a policy that no one shall come to the track with an illegal substance in their body."

Before 1983, when Bologna began to put together New York's program, testing was conducted under the "fitness" rule, which meant that when a jockey or driver was regarded as unfit to function, he or she was removed from the workplace. "If there was any question as to his fitness, he was taken off his mounts without any question, without any recourse by the jockey," Bologna said. "In looking back to see if there were any drug-abuse violations in New York State, I was able to find one case in 1978 at Belmont Park. Three jockeys were suspected of cocaine use, were tested positive for cocaine and PCP, and they were suspended and never heard from again."

A better system was needed, but the type of system was not clear. "We knew we wanted a random or general drug-testing program, but we knew we couldn't sell that at the time. We came up with a policy that we would only test those who we felt might be using drugs. Then the phrase, 'reasonable cause to believe' came up. I said, 'Wow! As a police-man, I had spent hours and days and weeks on the witness stand addressing reasonable cause to make an arrest.' I said we'd never get to the main issue, that a guy was using drugs. I sat down with John and said this reasonable cause is going to cause a lot of headaches. We're going to be from now to doomsday on whether we have cause to test him. We are a regulatory agency. We can make up any rule we want," Bologna said. "He said we'd strike that from our language and we will have a policy that says we will only test people when we believe they may be using drugs. That's a lot less restrictive than reasonable cause."

The policy "says this: A licensee that's asked to submit to a urine test, when directed, shall do so. And a licensee shall not have in his body an illegal, controlled substance. That's basically what it says. It doesn't address how we were going to do it; it doesn't state that we should have reasonable cause, or we should do it on a random or a general basis," Bologna said. "It's a broad rule, but our policy is such that we've main-tained it since 1983, to test when we have reason to believe a subject may be using drugs illegally."

Early in formulating a policy, Bologna realized that no drug-testing program at all was better than a bad testing program, and he set out to establish one with the highest standards. He also sought to enlist sup-port from the leaders of the group that most likely would be tested fre-quently, officials of the Jockeys' Guild. He met with Nick Jemas, then the national managing director and secretary of the Guild, and John Giovanni, the regional director for the New York tracks and ultimately Jemas's successor in the top administrative post. "I started to believe that we needed a different type of a program; we needed a program that would address the problems and why people use drugs, and afford indi-viduals the opportunity to take care of their problem. We met with the Jockeys' Guild, Nick Jemas and John Giovanni, and we proposed to them a program that included not only drug testing but education, prevention, and the possibility of rehabilitation," Bologna said.

"We got the cooperation from the Jockeys' Guild to the nth degree. They were very interested in addressing the problem back in '83. They weren't too interested in drug testing, though . . . later on, we got to be a little more comfortable with drug testing, especially when we read about athletes using drugs and some of our high officials using drugs. So drug testing is sort of now an acceptable term, but back then it was highly abrasive when you mentioned drug testing. But we attempted with the Jockeys' Guild's cooperation to start with an educational type of a program. We went out to the different tracks, Belmont and the harness tracks also, and we had a pharmacologist talking to the jocks and the horse people about the action of drugs in the body and why people use drugs and how to function in society without the use of drugs. With the jockeys in particular, we had nutritionists and dietitians come into Belmont, to talk to them about what they could do to maintain high energy and low weight without the use of chemicals, just by diet and exercise. We tried to address the problems of the jockeys in a positive way."

While the Jockeys' Guild assisted the racing board's efforts, NYRA officials were not as supportive in 1985. "They were trying to say at the time that the problem was no different than anywhere else in society, and that's the biggest lie you can give to this industry. It's greater back there than it is in society," said Bologna, who had undercover Division of Substance Abuse Services officers working on the backstretch that year. "What they reported to me was unbelievable. They reported epidemic proportions," he said. When drug problems at the tracks received wide publicity four years later, the NYRA conducted widespread raids on the backstretch. "They blitzed the backside, but after a week it was back to business," Bologna said. "The problem just came back. A problem like that is not going to go away by mere enforcement."

The good law-enforcement officer has his eyes and ears open, and Bologna wondered early in his tenure at the racing board why his investigators were getting marijuana positives but few for cocaine. His sources told him that cocaine use was becoming widespread. "So I started to ask some questions as to why we weren't picking up cocaine," he said. The answer was that thin-layer chromatography screening was not well-suited for detecting cocaine, and Bologna was advised to try enzyme-linked immunoassay screening. "As soon as we did that, boom, up popped the cocaine positives," he said.

In the 1980s, Bologna developed a large body of knowledge on drug testing, which now is carried out for the racing board by private laboratories. He insisted on professionalism in both decisions to test and chain of custody of samples. "It's like any other type of law-enforcement situation," he said. "A good detective is only as good as his information, and all of our investigators at the track are former law-enforcement people, either New York City detectives or county detectives or state police. That's why I have them handling the human-urine testing program, because they understand what evidence is. They understand completely the chain of custody."

A part of any responsible drug-testing program is that, if any question or uncertainty exists, the benefit of doubt is given to the person being tested. "It's the position of the racing board, and it's my position, that if a person has a problem with drugs or alcohol, that problem is so bad that if we don't get them today, we'll get them tomorrow. By testing him today, if we were able to discourage this guy's use of drugs even though we didn't suspend him or take any formal action, then we've done our job," Bologna said. "If we could deter people from using drugs just by being there, then we have a great program."

THE JOCK

Chris Wiley Antley had all the tools of a world-class jockey, and he also possessed a winning, mischievous smile that lit up a room. He was the natural, the golden boy, the free spirit. He was bright, enthusiastic, and eager to please. Even his introduction to horse racing has a storybook aspect. In his mid-teens, he was living in Elloree, South Carolina – midway between Charleston and Columbia – and was fishing at a pond where horses from the Elloree Training Center were grazed. "The guy that runs the place, Franklin Smith, asked me if I wanted a job doing the stalls. One thing led to another, and I decided I wanted to ride," Antley said.

During the summer of 1981, he worked at Delaware Park, and back home in South Carolina he galloped horses in the morning before school and returned to work at the barns after classes. "I was riding quarter horses at 16, on weekends at the South Carolina bush tracks," he said. He made his first pari-mutuel start at Maryland's Pimlico Race Course on June 1, 1983, and won his first race 11 days later aboard Vaya Con Dinero. He was the country's second-leading apprentice in 1984, behind Wesley Ward, and many observers believed that Antley was the better rider. In fact, Ward retired from riding a few years later after he grew in both height and weight. That spring, Antley moved to New Jersey, and he was Monmouth Park's leading jockey in 1984, 1985, and 1986. In 1985, he was the nation's leading rider by victories with 469, and he rode 31 stakes winners.

In late 1986, he made the move to riding full-time in New York, beginning with the winter meet, when many of the leading jockeys are in Florida. But he did so well that he continued through the year and was the top circuit's second-leading rider that year. Antley was in the fast lane, and it indeed was moving very fast. Too fast, in fact. Perhaps the first tip-off should have been in 1986, when he flunked a standard Breathalyzer test at the Meadowlands Racetrack in New Jersey. In an April, 1989, article in *The Thoroughbred Record*, Antley said his occasional marijuana use moved almost casually into cocaine in 1986. That year, "I started using cocaine more," he told Susan Finley. "At one time, I got to the point where I did a lot. I remember one time where probably four out of six days, I did cocaine – not consecutively – but I had picked it up and used it. I got so weak. And I guess what I did is what you call bottomed out." At a Rutgers-Florida college football game that October, Antley had drunk enough beer that he was taken off his mounts after failing the Breathalyzer test, which was administered to all jockeys and harness drivers in New Jersey. He was fined $250. But his problems with racing's authorities were only beginning.

COP AND JOCK

In the spring of 1988, Antley would ride Locust Hill Farm's Private Terms to victory in the Gotham Stakes and Wood Memorial, and they would go to Kentucky as the favorite for the Kentucky Derby. Locust Hill's colt made a modest challenge at the top of Churchill Downs's stretch but flattened out to finish ninth, about six lengths behind the victorious Winning Colors. At the time, the public did not know that

Antley had tested positive for marijuana in February.

Under procedures established by Van Lindt, Bologna, and the state racing board, Antley briefly surrendered his license. Bologna, who protects the confidentiality of licensees, did not discuss Antley's case – or that of any other person who tested positive. But he explained the procedures that the New York racing board has been using for at least a decade. The New York program conducts about 250 tests a year, or roughly one each racing day. The percentage of positives is relatively high, more than 20 percent, because investigators usually are acting on reliable intelligence. "For officials who are concerned with the race track, information flows their way every day, who might be involved with illegal drug use. If they use good judgment, they will have enough work to satisfy a pretty active drug-testing program," Bologna said. "We leave it to the people at the track to test people who they believe may be involved in illegal drug use."

The screening had snared Antley, and the jock began his relationship with the cop. "We ask him to do two things," Bologna said of the general procedure. "We ask him to surrender his license and to get into a program, at least to be evaluated. Then that program reports to us as to what they have found and whether that person is physically fit to return to work." Like many others in both enforcement and treatment, Bologna disputes the notion of "recreational" drug use. Any drug use is a problem use, and certainly Antley's occasional use became at one point almost daily. But the inquiry after a first positive seeks to establish the depth of the problem. "If the problem was marijuana, we wanted to know what the use was, a regular use of marijuana or an occasional use of marijuana," Bologna said. The state racing board mandates neither a specific course of treatment nor a specific program. "We direct that individual to the experts in the field of drug evaluation and treatment. We keep a catalog of all of the services that are available in the state of New York, and I also have a catalogue of all the services that are available in the country," Bologna said. "So when an individual in this predicament might say: 'But Dominick, I don't know where to go,' we could give him a number of places in his community to seek service. What we didn't want to get involved in was directing a licensee to a particular program, because we felt that we would then be vulnerable if, in the event that this individual failed in his rehabilitation, he could then say: 'Well, Dominick, you sent me to this particular program that was-n't suited for me. If you sent me someplace else, I probably would have succeeded.' So we didn't want to get involved in that kind of litigation, so we give them a number of places that they can go to."

The first-time offender gets his or her license back after the counselor recommends a return to work. "There's no report, there's no suspen-sion," Bologna said. "This is a confidential matter that basically lies between the individual and me at the racing board. There's nothing in the licensing folder. The only record is in my confidential records, and all of my files are mandated to be confidential."

During the initial period, the licensee does not ride or work in New York – or anywhere else. "If he goes to Philadelphia or the Meadowlands, he violates the agreement and then he is formally sus-pended," Bologna said. The initial time-out applies even to individuals who come to New York only for one race. "A very prominent rider shipped into New York a couple years ago. We had some information that he had problems, and we had to test him while he was here," Bologna said. "He came in for one race, we tested him, and he shipped right back out. He tested positive. I contacted him, and I told him I would treat him like a New York jockey as long as he didn't race. He had a tough time accepting that he couldn't race at his home track. I told him if I found out that he did, I would formally suspend him. He withdrew from racing and got himself straightened out. When I got reports from his counselor that he had passed urine tests, then I made him eligible to return to racing."

Bologna said he disagreed with jurisdictions that bar a licensee from racing in their state after a positive, but keep information of the posi-tive confidential and allow the individual to pursue their trade in another state. "That kind of disturbs me, because I don't think that's a responsible thing to do," he said.

After the first positive, Antley promised his agent, Drew Mollica, that he would avoid drugs, but it was a resolve that he proved unable to keep. Antley knew that he had to stay away from pot, so he drank – to the point where he was drinking heavily four or five months after his initial positive. Again, Antley was exposed to cocaine, and he used. "I picked it up as a social thing, and I was doing it, and it was like every two weeks, or every week, every three weeks, or whatever," he said in the 1989 *Thoroughbred Record* article. That summer, he began to use cocaine more regularly, but always mindful of the possibility he would be tested. "And I didn't think it was a problem. I didn't think it was any problem at all."

His career, from all appearances, was in high gear. He traveled to Japan and rode Virginia Kraft Payson's Salem Drive to victory in the Fuji International Stakes in mid-November. But inside the young man who had risen so quickly to the top of the sport, all was not well. As he flew back from Japan, he sat in his seat, wept as he watched the movie "Big," and wrote a letter to God. He wrote:

"Dear God,

"Since being young, I've come a long way so very fast and I'm not complaining about my success. But is this all, and should I live the rest of my life the way it is now? I've pulled away from living and enjoying every minute of my life. When I am old, will I sit and think about the things that just flew by unnoticed and the things I passed not doing and the people that sometimes feel imaginary? God, you've given me so much talent, opportunity, money, friends, and people who really care for me. And now do I really push all of this to its right fulfillment? And am I truly happy?"

No, he was not truly happy. The following day, he went out and bought cocaine. "And I used," he said. The next morning, he went to Aqueduct Race Track and was directed to provide a urine sample. "I went to the bathroom, and I knew I was positive," he said. He flew back to Japan, where Salem Drive was unplaced in the Japan Cup, and he learned of his suspension upon returning to New York. On November 24, 1988, under procedures of the New York Racing and Wagering Board, Chris Antley was suspended indefinitely.

Bologna noted that sometimes a second positive will occur two or three years after the first, but most often the second violation follows close on the heels of the initial positive. "Most of the time, if a guy is going to screw up, it's going to happen a short time after the first positive. Then that matter is handled by our legal section. That person is summarily suspended, and this is a formal record," he said.

Antley's response initially was to hide from the world, to use more and more cocaine with a clear intent of killing himself. But he found that his nose tissues broke down before he could administer a fatal overdose. On December 4, Antley entered the Smithers Alcoholism and Drug Treatment Center of St. Luke's-Roosevelt Hospital in New York City. He had reached out and seized a second chance. Antley came out of rehab on January 1, 1989, and was reinstated on January 25. He then enjoyed one of the sweetest runs a jockey has ever had. He won at least one race a day for 64 straight days at Aqueduct, from February 8 through May 1. On March 27, he rode five winners.

Through the rehabilitation period, Antley the top jock developed a close relationship with Bologna, the racing board's top cop. "Dominick was very supportive in every way. He was always there when I needed him, when I wanted to talk to him," Antley said in 1995. "Dominick is someone to me who always put a little bit extra oomph into his work as far as the people he dealt with. I had his home phone number. He was very loyal to me and stuck by me the whole time."

Antley's troubles did not end in early 1989, though. On September 26, 1989, only days before the first Louisville Conference, he surrendered his license voluntarily rather than face a third positive that almost certainly would have resulted in a lifetime ban. Antley admitted then that he was continuing to have substance-abuse problems and resumed his treatment at Smithers. He returned to riding on March 17, 1990, with three wins, two seconds, and a third. "They will not get my license again. I am back for good," Antley said on the day of his return from the wilderness. "I know I let a lot of people down before, especially myself." Less than 14 months later, Antley rode the wind, winning both Keeneland Race Course's Blue Grass Stakes and the Derby aboard Strike the Gold. Surely, Dominick Bologna won that Derby as much as Chris Antley. "I'll give anyone an opportunity to take control of their lives," Bologna said. "He did it for the betterment of the person," Antley said of Bologna. The rider shifted his tack to California in 1994 and was Santa Anita Park's third-leading rider with 73 victories, including a win (via disqualification) aboard Stuka in the Santa Anita Handicap. During the 1994 season, he rode his 3,000th career winner.

Without doubt, Bologna has given life-saving and career-saving opportunities to many individuals, including top harness driver Walter Case, who battled substance abuse in the early 1990s. For his work with the industry, the New York Standardbred owners association presented Bologna with its meritorious service award at a Yonkers Raceway dinner in 1994. "The president of the organization read a letter from four prominent harness drivers thanking me for some of the work we've done and for giving them the opportunity to turn their lives around. These were all hard-core addicts, and they were about to destroy their careers," Bologna said. "But we were able to interject ourselves and set them straight. Basically, they do it themselves. We hold their licenses over their head. We control their ability to continue in the sport. If they don't comply, then they're not going to continue in the sport, not here in New York or anywhere else. That's a tremendous motivating factor, at least, to have them expose themselves to experts in substance abuse. We'll bring the horse to water, so to speak, and now we hope that the experts get the horses to drink."

Chris Antley, Walter Case, and many others have tasted recovery, and they have expressed their gratitude to Bologna. "When people turn their lives around and they come up and thank you for helping them, that's very satisfying," he said.

Chapter 12

The Chaplaincy:
In a Place With No Name

David asked, "Is there still anyone left of the house of Saul to whom I
may show kindness for Jonathan's sake?"
Now there was a servant of the house of Saul whose name was Ziba,
and he was summoned to David. The king said to him, "Are you Ziba?"
And he said, "At your service!"
The king said, "Is there anyone remaining of the house of Saul to whom
I may show the kindness of God?" Ziba said to the king, "There remains
a son of Jonathan; he is crippled in his feet."
The king said to him, "Where is he?" Ziba said to the king, "He is in
the house of Machir son of Ammiel, at Lo-debar."
Then King David sent and brought him from the house of Machir son
of Ammiel, at Lo-debar.
Mephibosheth son of Jonathan son of Saul came to David, and fell on
his face and did obeisance. David said, "Mephibosheth!" He answered,
"I am your servant."
David said to him, "Do not be afraid, for I will show you kindness for
the sake of your father Jonathan; I will restore to you all the land of your
grandfather Saul, and you yourself shall eat at my table always."

2 Samuel 9:1-7
New Standard Revised Version

Before the race track had substance-abuse counselors, before the race
tracks had on-site lifestyle-improvement programs, before the race
tracks had the Ryan Family Foundation funds, the race tracks had the
chaplains. For more than a quarter century, chaplains have walked the
horse paths and the shedrows of North America's race tracks, where they

were frequently unheralded, sometimes unappreciated, and occasionally unpaid. But the race track was their calling, and they did their best in a place without a name – a place not unlike Lo-debar, which means a place with no name. From this place without a name, King David summoned Mephibosheth, the surviving son of Jonathan, who had saved David from the anger and spears of Jonathan's father, King Saul.

The Rev. Edward Hernandez was struck by the imagery of the passage from Second Samuel and gave it to his ministry at Gulfstream Park and Calder Race Course in Miami. Lo-debar is an alternate transliteration of the Hebrew lo d'var, literally "no word." Through their time on the track, the chaplains have sought to bring dignity to a population that generally has little self-esteem, to provide a message of hope in an environment that one medical professional described as "toxic."

Dr. Wayne E. Oates, senior professor of the Southern Baptist Seminary in Louisville and professor in the University of Louisville School of Medicine's Department of Psychiatry and Behavioral Sciences, discussed the role of the chaplain at the inaugural Conference on Alcohol and Drug Abuse Programs for the Horse Racing Industry at Louisville in 1989. "The chaplain works within the tensions that exist between his or her faith and ethics, and the prevailing standards of the institution where he or she is chaplain. Military standards, hospital standards, prison standards, police force standards, fire department standards, race track standards," said Dr. Oates, who many years earlier had analyzed his own behavior and given the word "workaholic" to the language. "Their work with individuals and groups concentrates on the very personal life of those individuals and groups. However, they are caught in the context in the race track industry where somebody wins and there has to be a celebration. You celebrate with alcohol, as you said a while ago. The chaplain, I think if he or she is really with it, attends that celebration and has that in common with Jesus, who attended the celebration of a marriage. However, the tension is that the chaplain is not in charge of the institution. They don't have power and control over policy-making and process-making. If a chaplain is hooked on power and the capacity to run the show, as many ministers are, this disqualifies him to work in that setting because he is definitely not in charge. However, he is in the context, and he has to work like salt in the bread we eat, or, better, like the leaven in the lump."

Chaplains always have trod where angels feared to go, and the clergy's tasks have become all the more difficult with the epidemic of alcoholism and drug abuse on the backstretches of North America. In the last decade, they have received assistance from professional substance-abuse counselors, although the merging of the efforts have not always been harmonious. Still, many chaplains, including Pennsylvania's long-time race track chaplain Nicholas Salios and the Rev. Jim Watson in New York, have worked hand-in-hand with the counselors at their tracks. One of the lessons that counselor Lori Weinegar had to learn when she went to work at Philadelphia Park was how to interact with Nick Salios, who served the Pennsylvania tracks through the 1980s and the 1990s. "All these years the chaplain was doing the drug and alcohol work, and here I was doing the drug and alcohol work in some sense, taking a piece of his job from him," Weinegar said at the 1989 Louisville Conference. "Nick Salios and I had to talk about that and really had to work out our relationship so that today it is really quite complementary, and we work together."

In all probability, the race track always has had its chaplains, although they were not always ordained. They were racetrackers who had found faith in God and, in the best traditions of Christianity, sought to share the message with others. It was, in fact, a racetracker who brought ordained ministers onto the backstretch. The Rev. Homer Tricules, who served as executive director of the Race Track Chaplaincy of America in the late 1980s and early 1990s, recounted the story at the 1989 Louisville Conference. The organization was the brainchild of Horace "Salty" Roberts, "who was a racetracker and alcoholic – and a few other things. He reached the end of his rope, was ready to take his life. He got on his knees and prayed. He made a serious commitment of his life to Christ, and everything changed," Tricules said. "He prayed for two or three years, and he said: 'Lord, what will you have me do with my life now? Shall I leave the race track, because of all that goes on here, or shall I stay?' And he was given the leading from above to stay at the race track and to help those with whom he worked. He was given the mission of placing a chaplain at every race track in the country. Most of us would say that's impossible, I can't afford it, or some such thing as that. But not Salty. Being a man of real faith – not religion, faith – Salty said: 'Yes, Lord.'

"And so he began whispering in the ears of the preachers wherever he worshiped. He was on the circuit between Florida and New Jersey. In Florida, he whispered in his preacher's ear down there; in New Jersey, he whispered in my ear up here. I wasn't going to go out to the race track--that devil's den! That's a place of iniquity! I should go there and taint my testimony? No, you see, I was a self-righteous snob. I couldn't do that. After two years of pleading with me, he finally got me out of bed at 4:30 one morning – and that took an act of God, believe me – got me out to the race track by 5:30. I spent most of the day there in the stable area and some time on the frontside. I came home, and I wept. I was ashamed, and I was repentant. I thank God today for the board of deacons I had at the First Baptist Church in Long Branch, because when I went to them and told them what I found and told them I thought we should begin a little mission out at the race track, they didn't back off. They said, 'Well, Pastor, that's what it's all about. Let's do it.' And so, about 1970, both in Florida and in New Jersey, some of us began ministering at race tracks. Phil Iselin was the first president and general manager and chief executive officer of a race track (Monmouth Park) to say yes, in the late '60s – opened the door and said, 'Come.' So we went."

The Race Track Chaplaincy was formally organized in 1970 and incorporated in 1972. The chaplains went on the backstretches and found a population that generally was not served by traditional churches – a group that many churches would wish to avoid. "We are there for everybody at the race track. We zero in on the stable-area personnel," Tricules said. "We hope the time will come when the industry learns that you cannot have a circus without the clowns. Take away the stable area personnel and the industry falls apart. And yet, they're the last ones to get any thought or any consideration. Slowly, that's changing, and I'm glad for that, and I encourage that change to continue. That's where our chaplains zero in, the stable area personnel. But when the word spreads that a chaplain is there who means business – he's not a fly-by-night, he's not a kook, he's for real – the ministry spreads. People on the frontside call for the chaplain. Car-lot attendants, jockeys, valets, managerial staff, the industry management, chief executive officers, racing officials, security personnel – they all learn there is a chaplain, and they all call for him when there is a need. So our ministry, you see, is broad-based like any pastor's ministry in a church, except it's in a separated community." In that community, a community where loneliness and despair were daily companions of many people, Tricules said he found the divine spark and the truth of American psychologist and philosopher William James's statement – quoted by Oates – that there is very little difference between people, but they make a great deal of what little difference there is.

Tricules recounted his experience with Hubert, an alcoholic race-tracker, at the 1989 Louisville Conference. "Hubert carried his vodka in a Vaseline Intensive Care bottle tucked in his belt like this. I guess he thought nobody would know it was vodka, but everybody knew. He had never missed a service. At the end of every service, he would tell me the same thing: 'I don't believe a word of it.' But he kept coming. We had a policy. Now, one of the things chaplains do is to build bridges between the race track and the community. And so we invited various groups to come in to our services. We have church choirs come, we have guest speakers come," Tricules said. "Friends are made, and that's so important. Whereas before, racetrackers would have been cold-shouldered out of local churches, and now they're being received into local churches. Why? Because the people of the churches are learning race-trackers don't have horns and tails; they're people like everybody else and they need God's love. So we build bridges.

"Hubert's policy was to find the prettiest woman that came with the church group, to sit next to her in the service and try to make time. They don't teach you how to handle that in seminary. So, we were in a service down at Garden State Park, it was February, it was bitter cold outside, icy, snowy, and Hubert went through his usual routine. He found this woman – made somebody change their seat so he could sit next to her – and during the singing of the hymns and the praying and so on, he went through his usual routine. Time came for the reading of the Scripture and time came for the message. I got about five minutes into the sermon, and Hubert stands up in the last row – you'll excuse the language now, I'm quoting – puts his hands way up over his head says to me in the middle of the sermon: 'You're full of shit!' Well, they never taught me in seminary how to handle that, either. I was so furious and so upset, I didn't know what to do. Hubert left, and I went, 'Thank you, Lord.' But he came back; it was obvious he just went outside to get a swig. He came back.

"Well, we got through the service, I still don't know how. I guess it was by God's grace. We got through the service, we had our time of refreshments – the church groups bring sandwiches and doughnuts and coffee and so on – and everything was fine, and I stayed away from Hubert because I was angry with him. Wouldn't you be? Well, after the refreshment time was over, the church people were leaving, we started to clean up, got everything in order, and who was the last one in the room with me but Hubert. And he comes over to me and he says: 'Would you give me a lift down to my barn?' And I looked up and silently, I said: 'Lord, you gotta have that second mile.' But he probably wouldn't have made it, because he was so cock-eyed anyway. So I put him in the car, and I took him down to the barn.

"I stopped at the barn and I said, 'You're here.' He looks over to me, and he says: 'Would you walk me to my room?' And I looked up and said: 'Lord, you gotta have the third mile, too? Thanks a lot!' So okay, I got out of the car, I walked Hubert over to his room, and it was like the Keystone Kops – he was so looped, he could hardly find the keyhole in the door. But he did, went in as I stood there, walked to the other side of the room, bent down, and picked up something I couldn't see till he turned around. And there he carries over to me a beautiful flowering potted plant. And he hands it to me and he says: 'This is for you and your family. Because you're the only one who's loved me.' Do you know how I felt? About that big. Who was I, to be upset with this man, who was alone, who had an alcohol problem, who came to my service, whom no one cared about – and I'm supposed to be a Christian, and I was angry with him? I felt about that big. That was a new beginning for me. And I'm sure our chaplains could tell you many stories like that. We're there to love the people. And I'm not talking about a sentimental, emotional feeling. I'm talking about being there for them when nobody else wants them or wants to hear about them."

Salty Roberts, whose persistence led to creation of the Race Track Chaplaincy of America, was honored in 1993 with the inaugural Dominion Award, presented by Dogwood Stable's Anne and Cot Campbell to celebrate the "unsung heroes" of the race track. Roberts, who went to the race track at age 15 in 1945, certainly is an unsung hero who launched an organization of unsung heroes, who very often were unpaid heroes. "You know," one chaplain said in 1994, "if you're willing to do it, the race tracks will let you work for free." Chaplains always have existed in a financial purgatory between parsimony and penury, and the national organization ran into difficult times in the 1990s despite assistance from the Ryan foundation and such leading figures as jockey Patrick Day. Many chaplains found that they were dependent on their own resources, or their church, or the track to pay for the work of converting despair into hope.

Religious conversion – some within evangelical Christianity refer to it as being "born again" – is one path to recovery. Indeed, the 12 steps of Alcoholics Anonymous emphasize a belief in a "Power greater than ourselves," and both Christian and Jewish scholars have found the 12 steps to be within their traditions. Dr. Oates, in discussing his experiences with conversions related to substance abuse, said he had discerned three or four distinct types of conversions. In his 1989 presentation, he said that, "when you dig in under the biblical meaning of the word conversion, it's very, very simple. It means to turn, to turn around, to make a 180-degree change of direction. An about-face, in military terms, has occurred: An about-face in life. It's a matter not of changing the very structure of a human being, but of taking that very same human being and changing the total direction of his or her life."

He said that, in studying 20 cases of alcoholics who just quit due to a religious conversion, he found four distinctive types of conversion: the restrictive conversion, the social-approval religious conversion, the pit-of-despair conversion, and the act of surrender. In the restrictive conversion, he said, "this person was for real. He or she organized their lives around the revelation of God and, if they were Christians, they did so around the person of Jesus Christ. If they were Jewish, they did so around the people of God who have a mission and await a Messiah. Yet, the restrictive-conversion person cannot abide people who disagree with them. They scour land and sea to make converts. Yet they insist that those converts have a religious experience precisely like their own. These converts can help some people, usually dependent people. But the hostile, aggressive person rejects them. This person has been converted from alcoholism, but one wonders whether or not this particular form of religion has not become a substitute addiction. And religion can become not faith in Christ or faith in God, but faith in religion. It can become an addiction in its own right. They are compulsive about their evangelism. They have simply shifted the focus of their compulsiveness.

"Then, there is the ineffective religious conversion. I would call this social-approval religious conversion. A person is converted to the companionship of the church as a social institution. Yet he or she is uncommitted at the core of their being and simply changes the company they keep, which is a good step to take. As I spoke to one alcoholic, I said, 'Your drinking is killing you, and you can do something about it.' He said, 'Well, all the people I know drink as much as I do.' I said to him: 'Well, probably so, but you're going around with a bunch of drunks.' Now this person in this kind of conversion changes his company, but he does not really change his alcoholism. They do not quit their substance abuse. They do separate from drinking buddies and maintain face with the church. But they remain torn beings who teach Sunday school during the weekends and drink during the week. Their drinking becomes all the more an isolated, lonely experience.

"Now the third kind of conversion that we found was the person who had a total response of faith in God born out of the pit of despair of their substance abuse. Now, I'd like to suggest some language. We talk about hitting bottom. But we overlook a grand concept in both the Old and the New Testament of the pit. There are pit experiences. You could even say that Joseph, when he was thrown into a pit, a literal pit, had a transformation of his life. Before that, he had grandiose dreams about ruling his brothers and his mother and father, that all of them would bow down to him. But after that he never dreamed any more. He interpreted other people's dreams," Oates said. "They share themselves, but eagerly learn from other people. And the grandiosity has been replaced by humorous humility. They become honest, truth-telling, levelers with other people. They have a heightened sense of self-esteem, but it grows out of a sense of having received the grace of God."

Another type of conversion, he said, "is what we call a psychosocial act of surrender in conversion. And the man who did most of his work in the 1950s and 1960s, Harry M. Tiebold, a psychiatrist, wrote two very helpful articles on this. One was the act of surrender in the treatment of alcoholism, and the other one was the role of conversion in the treatment of alcoholism. In this, he says that a person comes to a point when his unconscious forces of defiance and grandiosity actually cease to function effectively. One of the things that all of us have in common with alcoholics and drug abusers is that we have our own share of grandiosity and defiance. But when those defenses and deceptions cease to function effectively, then is when conversion happens to them. And when this happens, the person is opened up to reality. To quote Tiebold, they can listen and learn without conflict and fighting back. They are receptive to life and not antagonistic to life as it is. They experience a relatedness or an at-one-ness with people, and they develop a source of inner peace and serenity, the possession of which frees them from the compulsion to drink. They cease to fight life and accept it."

Cooperation between counseling professionals and chaplains has produced results in New York and elsewhere. Their cooperation gives the alcoholic or drug abuser two doors to recovery. People who would find recovery through a chaplain would use that route, but there would have to be another route for people who have had experiences that would prevent them from returning to their religious affiliation.

Dr. Edward Hernandez's Lo-debar Ministry has sought to provide counseling and treatment within the context of the ministry. As senior pastor of Christ Community Church in Hollywood since the early 1980s, a part of his ministry was Gulfstream Park in Hallandale. Beginning in 1984, the ministry has had an on-track substance-abuse clinic operating out of the backstretch chapel. "I think that back in the Dark Ages that it used to be a thought that science and Christianity could not walk hand in hand. That's just not so. We have much that we can learn from one another," he said. "We have a therapist on staff, a certified psychologist, and he works with us, gives us three hours a day, and he handles areas that we feel we can't. That's one thing that chaplains, I think, have to learn immediately is that you cannot handle all of their problems just with the spiritual. We have a holistic approach. Paul taught us that man is a trichotomy, he is body, soul, and spirit. You certainly wouldn't let a clergyman decide to do open-heart surgery on you. No, that's not his area of expertise. His realm is the realm of the soul, spiritual things. It needs to be confined to that. Sometimes pride and ego want us to get into areas we have no business dealing with. But there are people in the psychological realm. There also is the social realm," he said.

Hernandez built his program by first developing a sense of trust with

Gulfstream's security department and then persuading Gulfstream president Douglas Donn that the results were worth a substantial investment by the track. With Donn's support, Hernandez built a substantial program that included medical and dental care, and he has cooperated with the track's security director and the Thoroughbred Racing Protective Bureau agent at Gulfstream to create an information and education program promoting the drug-free shedrow.

Some chaplains, including Tricules, said they had difficulty cooperating with the counselors in the early years of the on-track programs because it seemed that they had differing agenda. While urging cooperation, Tricules and other chaplains did not believe that their concerns were being addressed by the counselors. "One of the things that distresses so many of the chaplains is that frequently drug and alcohol counselors will leave God outside the door. That distresses all of us," he said in 1989. Oates, in responding to Tricules's concerns, said the chaplains should look to how the counselors express religious belief through their actions and behavior, rather than an articulate expression of their faith. "There is so much to be done, there's no need for competition," he said.

The chaplaincy also has opportunities for cooperation with the communities outside the stable gate, and that cooperation can yield significant resources and gains for the on-track clergy. In the future, perhaps, this cooperation will alter the isolated lifestyle of the backstretch.

Chapter 13

America's Fastest Athlete

What is America's fastest athlete? Many people think of the Thoroughbred, capable of running a mile and a quarter in two minutes on a good day. But despite the renown of such horses as Secretariat and Seattle Slew, the Thoroughbred is not America's fastest athlete. Fastest by a considerable margin is the Quarter Horse, a breed that is as American as apple pie. From a standing start, the Quarter Horse will reach 55 mph in a few strides, while a Thoroughbred's top speed is approximately 48 mph. The Quarter Horse is quick out of the gate, and the races down a quarter-mile straightaway are over in 20 seconds or so. For substantial parts of America, mostly in the West, Quarter Horse racing is a sporting staple. In all, the sport is represented at 109 tracks in the western United States, the western provinces of Canada, and Mexico. Oklahoma's Remington Park and the new tracks in Texas have separate Quarter Horse meets, although most often the Quarter Horses race on mixed cards, containing some Thoroughbred races, some Quarter Horse races, and perhaps some Arabian or Appaloosa races.

Overseeing Quarter Horse racing is the American Quarter Horse Association, which is the registry and marketer of the world's most popular type of horse. In 1993, the American Quarter Horse Association registered more than 100,000 horses (Thoroughbred registrations that year were 35,405), and circulation of the association's monthly magazine, Quarter Horse Journal, exceeds 70,000. To be sure, not all Quarter Horses – or even a majority of them – find their way onto the race track, but racing is a distinctive, important aspect of the breed and a highly visible way of promoting the Quarter Horse. In short, this is a very big and powerful organization, and it has placed itself behind efforts to combat alcohol and drug abuse in its racing. And, while the AQHA has no regulatory authority, when it speaks, a lot of people raise their heads and listen.

In the 1990s, the AQHA has been quick out of the gate in becoming involved with alcohol and drug programs, and it is a shining example of how organizations can make a difference in the struggle to achieve a drug-free workplace in racing. Other organizations and institutions have certainly made their contribution. Several state regulatory agencies and the regulators' organization, the Association of Racing Commissioners International, have worked to combat substance abuse through their own functions, and academic institutions – most notably the University of Louisville Department of Equine Administration and the University of Arizona's Race Track Industry Program – have furnished educational resources to the regulators through stewards' schools. Unquestionably one of the most important concepts developed at the Conferences on Alcohol and Drug Abuse Programs for the Horse Racing Industry was offered by Paul Berube, president of the Thoroughbred Racing Protective Bureau, who proposed an educational program for first-time race-track workers.

On-site addiction-treatment programs began in the Thoroughbred community, and a scheduling conflict prevented AQHA officials from attending the first Louisville Conference in 1989. But Dr. Robert Lawrence, who heads the University of Louisville's equine program, applied pressure to Dan Fick, the AQHA's senior director of racing, to attend the 1990 Louisville Conference. "Bob Lawrence kind of twisted my arm to go and see it," Fick said in 1995. "When I went and got a true understanding for what the problem was on the backside, I realized we needed to get more actively involved in providing some sort of assistance program to these people, other than what was already there, which was very limited. I ended up shortly thereafter on the substance abuse committee of the American Horse Racing Federation."

Unlike Thoroughbred racing, which seems to have many voices shouting all at once for attention, Quarter Horse racing has tended to speak with one voice when presenting itself to the public. That has increased the effectiveness of an organization without actual regulatory powers. "We're smaller, and we couldn't afford to have a track association and a breed registry and an owners association," said Fick, who came to the AQHA from the University of Arizona's Race Track Industry Program. "Historically, when something needed to be done, everyone said, 'Let's get AQHA to do it,' because we have the large base of support from the standpoint of having the rest of the industry. That's why we're more cohesive. We always thought it was better to work together when we're small. To splinter ourselves would be death to the industry."

The large membership base also helps to get people's attention. Although the AQHA lacks rule-making authority, "we suggest and encourage," Fick said. "But when you have as many members as we have, you can suggest and encourage pretty loudly. We've done some things in Texas. We were able to suggest to the Texas Racing Commission that they adopt the charity-day rule that most states have, but we made sure that the first charity day went to the organizations providing benevolence on the backside rather than having it go to local charities in the town. This has helped to get the Race Track Chaplaincy off the ground in Texas, which has been the leader on substance abuse on the backsides in Texas. At least, they were the only ones we could work through initially. We've done that. Although we do not have any regulatory authority, we can be pretty effective in encouraging people to do things that are beneficial to the industry."

Fick said he believed the efforts are bearing fruit. "I am seeing a significant increase in the understanding at the track-management and the horsemen's-association levels. The staff people that are involved day to day, they know there is a problem within the industry. It's different wherever you go. The big city tracks are different from the tracks out West, particularly the tracks at county fairs. Quarter Horse racing tends to be more of a family-type operation.

Therefore, the family values create a situation where you probably don't have as much drug and alcohol problems as you find back East. But we have plenty of problems."

A new drug and alcohol treatment program, the New Mexico Winner's Circle Foundation, was founded in 1993 and launched in 1994. By early 1995, the program had 17 people in recovery at Sunland Park. "Two years ago, that would not have been happening. We're seeing a lot of people receive the treatment they need. The more we see people getting the treatment, the more we find people needing it, or tracks expressing a need. We'd like to have a program like that in Arizona."

As others have noted, the on-track program must look at the problem from many angles, because the backstretch troubles do not spring from a single source. "I don't think there's a track in America that's drug-free. It's different kinds of problems," Fick said. "The chaplain who works at Remington Park, with a straight Quarter Horse meet and with a straight Thoroughbred meet, has different people to deal with. The chaplain at Bandera Downs, who also is a drug and alcohol counselor, said he has an entirely different situation down there. He does more counseling on family problems than on substance abuse. You can't limit it to substance abuse. You need a well-rounded employee assistance program that deals with all aspects of the problems that they have."

Stewards schools are one of the most productive strategies for making racing officials aware of the problems that substance abuse cause them and the tracks where they work. The University of Lousville's Department of Equine Administration was the first to offer a drug-and-alcohol component in its stewards-accreditation program in 1989. In addition to basic information about alcohol and drug abuse, the program stresses "communication, cooperation, common sense, and comprehension in that the communication between the steward and the accredited drug counselor is necessary," said Bernard J. Hettel, executive director of the Kentucky Racing Commission and an active participant in several of the Louisville Conferences.

The first steward schools were held by the AQHA in the mid-1970s. At first, the schools were a response to the two worlds of Quarter Horse racing, pari-mutuel tracks and those meets without legal betting. "We've never really regulated racing, but we went into the nonpari-mutuel states," said Fick. "There was a ton of racing going on at that time, and most of it was Quarter Horse racing. It was pretty well organized, and they were running for a lot of money. These horses would run six or seven times, have four or five wins, and run out $50,000 to $100,000. Then they'd show up at a pari-mutuel meet in Louisiana or New Mexico or California as non-starters. We went in and made sure some minimum standards were maintained at these race tracks, pointing toward having a uniform, level playing field where we could recognize some results, grade the horses, and give people some past performances. In the course of doing that, we had to educate stewards. So we started the stewards school." The AQHA, which also maintains the performance records for the sport, continued the schools into the 1980s. "About 1984, we saw a lot more pari-mutuel stewards starting to come to our school," said Fick, who has been with the AQHA since 1981. Beginning in 1989, the AQHA started holding the school in conjunction with the University of Arizona, and it turned the project over to the Tucson school in 1993. After attending the 1990 Louisville Conference, Fick invited co-author Dr. Curtis L. Barrett to make a presentation to the AQHA's leaders, and a substance-abuse component was added to the stewards school. "It was something that needed to be added to the curriculum," Fick said. "It was a problem we found the stewards were having to deal with. They were asking questions we couldn't answer."

Through a decade of substance-abuse programs, several organizations have made noteworthy contributions. On the regulatory side, the Association of Racing Commissioners International has adopted model substance-abuse rules that are at once firm and humane, in that they recognize the possibility of relapse in a recovery program. The model rule is a modified "three strikes and you're out" policy, and in principle offers the opportunity for one, uniform regulation to be adopted in every racing jurisdiction. With one rule, racing jurisdictions would be one step closer to a "passport" system in which both individuals and their recovery efforts would move from on-track programs at one jurisdiction to another state or locale.

This approach was endorsed at the 1990 Louisville Conference by John Giovanni, national managing director of the Jockeys' Guild and chairman of the American Horse Racing Federation's Substance Abuse Committee. He noted that the Jockeys' Guild opposes random testing, because his organization does not believe it pinpoints those in difficulty and thus posing a danger to jockeys. "I think the biggest problem is the diversity in the rules and regulations around the United States. We have a lot of people that fall between the cracks," he said. In one state that conducts random testing, "when they come up with a positive, the first thing they do is send them a letter from the executive director, telling him he's on notice. Basically, what that means is pack your tack and go someplace else, and ultimately what that does is makes him somebody else's problem. They sweep their dirty laundry across the state lines. He becomes somebody else's problem; and because of the confidentiality that's also involved in the rule, this racing commission can't even forward ahead and tell the racing commission in the state where this person is now plying his trade, that he, in fact, has an alcohol or a drug problem. And that is a big problem because what happens is there's usually an incident before we find out that he does have a problem and can force him to address his problem," Giovanni said.

"The Jockeys' Guild has taken the position that the first time somebody comes up with a positive, he should be sent up for an evaluation so at least we know what we're dealing with. This guy or girl, is this person a first-time user, smoking marijuana? Or is this person heavily into crack? Is this person drinking a quart of scotch a day? What exactly are we dealing with here? And I don't think you can do that without a professional evaluation. I think once the person is evaluated and we feel that his situation is nonaddictive or it is such that it can be controlled under a certain environment and he's allowed to participate back in the industry, he should only be allowed to come back in if he agrees to further testing and testing at the discretion of the racing commission or the stewards, be that once a day, twice a day, once a week, once a month, whenever; but it's at their discretion. And in our opinion, this helps to keep people on their toes. They don't know if they're going to be tested. They're not sure when it's going to come. They're not sure that if before the first race they have to give a test, and they might have to give another one after the fifth. So we think that this helps these people, that some-one comes up with a positive a second time, we recommend that he's out of the business for at least six months and that he definitely is referred to rehab. Quite possibly a person is referred to rehab for a first positive. For a third positive, we don't think they should be in the business any longer. It's a pretty stiff penalty, pretty tough thing to do. And it's basically that people have to know that they're either going to have to face their problem or they shouldn't be involved in a business where they're putting other people's lives at risk.

"I don't think I could begin to tell you what it's like to sit in the starting gate and look over at somebody who's staring up in space. It's a dangerous enough business as it is, and we don't want people out there who are not in charge of their faculties. One of the resolu-tions that we passed at our board meeting last December was that if anybody in the jockeys room was noted to have or thought to have a problem, we would ask them to come forward and seek some help. If he refused to come forward and seek some help, then any two jockeys in that one room would report him to the proper authori-ties, be it the stewards or racing commission, and demand that they test him and demand that he seek assistance if, in fact, he needs it. It's kind of harsh measures, but it's a tough business. We have in excess of 2,500 injuries per year. We've had two people killed on average every year. The Jockeys' Guild has 46 permanently disabled people that we take care of, (47 as of late 1994), and I like to think that all that was just because it's a dangerous sport and not because somebody was under the influence of drugs or alcohol and caused that person the suffering that they have today. I just hope that I never have to deal with another widow or fatherless children, and I hope I never see anybody else in a wheelchair again. And especially I hope that if it does happen, it isn't because of somebody abusing alcohol or drugs."

Giovanni's statement in 1990 recognized that testing has become a part of the battle against drug abuse, and regulators similarly see its value as deterrence. Rear Admiral Paul Mulloy launched the Navy's war on drugs in the early 1980s with a program that included testing and drug-sniffing dogs. "You've got the little (testing) kit in front of everybody, so it's working as a deterrent just being there," he said at the 1991 Louisville Conference. "I remember when I brought these things into the Navy, and I got 600 of them plus the dogs that go snooping around. I said a kit that doesn't work and a dog with a cold in his nose will keep 70 percent of that stuff off the ship."

In California, testing was used creatively in a commission-mandated program involving Patrick Valenzuela, a talented jockey – he won the 1989 Kentucky Derby and Preakness Stakes aboard Sunday Silence and has ridden six Breeders' Cup winners – who twice has been suspended for cocaine positives. Dennis Hutcheson, who served as the California Horse Racing Board's executive secretary in the early 1990s, explained in 1991 the procedure that was developed involving Valenzuela, the Winners' Foundation, and the CHRB. Hutcheson noted that the Winners Foundation and its president, Richard Smith, were instrumental in developing the racing board's approach to the situation.

As Valenzuela's six-month suspension neared its conclusion, the board wrestled with the question of how to handle his reinstatement. "Do we give him a hearing as we're required under the law and let him show rehabilitation, and certainly he could have done that. License him, put him back into the backside, and he's faced with the same problems again," Hutcheson said. "We didn't feel that that was the answer. I met with Rick, I met with Patrick, and I met with the stewards, and we developed a program that we used Patrick with," Hutcheson said.

"Basically you have two parts of this program. One is drug testing, and you've heard that (it is) a deterrent, and that's all it is. It's a deterrent. It's one tool to be used in establishing a rehab and prevention program for alcohol and drug abuse. The other is establishing that rehab and prevention program and through the services of the Winners Foundation and other programs such as that to provide those services. So we have set up an agreement with those licensees that have fallen under the prey of drugs that a licensee agrees to provide a urine sample to the California Horse Racing Board at least three times a week, every other day while licensed in California or through the term of the license or probation in accordance with the steward's ruling," he said. If the urine sample were not provided for any reason, the CHRB would presume that the sample would have tested positive for drugs or alcohol "And I think the key there is alcohol because first you drink a couple of beers and then you move on to cocaine or marijuana or other drugs," Hutcheson said.

Beyond the testing, the licensee agrees to participate in a rehabilitation program through the Winners Foundation. During the period of the agreement, the individual must attend and participate in a minimum of five 12-step recovery meetings per week. The 12-step program must be approved by the Winners Foundation case worker, and at least four of the weekly meets must be of the participation or discussion type," said Hutcheson, who was dismissed from his position in 1993 for his handling of a equine-medication matter. Valenzuela unfortunately has been unable to continue his career without problem. He repeatedly has been suspended and, in late 1996, allowed his license to lapse. In early 1997, Valenzuela reapplied for a license, but without any assurance that his application would be approved.

Education is a valuable tool in combating substance abuse, and the Manitoba Racing Commission began identifying and training backstretch mentors. Dr. William Jacyk, a physician, explained the training program at the 1991 Louisville Conference. "What we've done is actually have had two short courses over the last two years. That is, we've trained what we now call peer advocates or counselors in the backstretch, representatives of all disciplines: trainers, jockeys, a steward, security people; and they are now the first contact individuals," he said. "The interesting thing that's happened with the peer advocates is many people talked about the short course and the benefits that it brings about. We trained them in two separate bunches. They have now decided to form a community of their own in the backstretch. This is a combination of people who are in their own twelve-step recovery programs but also people who are sensitive to twelve-step recovery, and they have actually become our after-care program. They are people well known in the backstretch and are approachable, and I think the final thing that happened just this past summer is one of our trainees is also the race-track chaplain, so that the whole program has come together."

Without question, one of the Louisville Conferences' most provocative ideas was advanced by Paul Berube, the TRPB president who proposed that a short course of orientation and training be offered to all new licensees on the race track. He noted that the new race track employee often shows up at the stable gate, is hired by a trainer, gets his or her license, and disappears into the culture of the backstretch without any exposure to what is expected of them in the new job environment. The course also could provide information on substance abuse – there is a lot of ignorance about alcohol and drugs out there – and introduce the new track employee to security officials, the chaplain, and members of the on-track drug and alcohol program. Berube said the program, "be it Thoroughbred, Standardbred, Quarter Horse or Arabians, can take a relatively simple – and I think low-cost – step to foster an unimpaired stable-area work force."

For a 1991 Louisville Conference session on his proposal, Berube invited William L. Ramsey, a former TRPB agent and Pimlico Race Course executive who had become manager of safety, security, and services for McCormick & Co. in Baltimore. McCormick had saved millions of dollars through its training and quality-assurance programs, and Ramsey outlined some of the essentials of a good training program. Backstretch orientation would highlight the traditions and pleasures of the horse racing industry as well as suitable warnings about antisocial behavior and substance abuse. McCormick, he said, has formal training programs that include written materials and oral presentations, and it has informal programs such as mentoring. "Don't discount informal programs, mentoring or coaching or sponsors," he said. "What that means is that we have somebody, a physical person. We can go up, grab them by the shoulder and say, we need help. 'You're my sponsor, you're my coach, you're my mentor. Please tell me what I'm supposed to do in this situation.' Well, that's real important to have a person like that. It's always great to have somebody to ask that one question of."

Ramsey and most training professionals put little stock in the racing-industry standby, on-the-job training. "Well, OJT is the most used and probably the least effective, believe it or not, of any of these programs when you're really trying to impart information," he said. Why? Principally, because a training program requires structure, both in its design and its presentation.

In designing a training program, Ramsey advised that the course fit the employee. "Consider the education and ability to learn. Well, you're not going to be able to do brain surgery in a stable area; but you can tailor your program to the educational and to the learning ability of the people that you're trying to give the information to. You don't have to make it so simple that any three-year-old can understand it, but you have to make it simple enough that everybody can understand it. The program has to be tailored to fit the environment that you're in," he said.

"Keep it simple. Provide clear and concise information. That's real important. Sometimes we get carried away with what we want to give out. Sometimes I get carried away when I give a presentation, and I want to give you more than you're ready to accept. So keep it clear. Keep it concise. Don't give out more than you're willing to give out. Don't give out more than you're willing to explain, and make sure it's just enough so that people can understand it and carry it away with them. Make it relevant. Don't tell what it's like in Hialeah when you're at NYRA. Make it relevant to your situation; and when you do the medium such as videotapes, slides, try to keep those within your own organization, if that's possible, so that you can say,

'Well, this is what happens in our backstretch.' Follow up with additional training," Ramsey said.

Berube's concept also was endorsed by Russell Jones Jr., a thoughtful horseman and breeder who served on the Pennsylvania Horse Racing Commission in the 1980s and 1990s. He suggested that the orientation be devised outside the state bureaucracy, with the government acting as catalyst for the process. "I think that the commission can, in an informal way, require it, and it can be structured so that all of the participants in our industry participate in it, and I think the commission's in a position to gently nudge everybody to participate. But I think that the HPBA, the track managements, the chaplains, the jockeys, the frontside, unions – there are so many participants that should be part of this program, and I think it's the commission's role to gently nudge them into participation in this. I think the commission can make sure it does get done," he said. "This can be such a low-cost thing. Really it's going to be a cost in people's time only, and there are none of those individual organizations that I've mentioned, individual groups, that won't give time. I'm sure of that. They will give time because they know what we're talking about here is a good thing. I think the only thing that's important is that it be professionally spelled out how it's going to be done so that when they're giving time, they're not wasting time. I think the main thing here is we don't want to do it big. We want to do it small and do it well."

The Ryan Family Foundation's money provided North America's nascent drug and alcohol programs with a jump start that is reminiscent of "America's fastest horse" bursting from the starting gate. But the battle against addictions is not won in the 20 seconds of a Quarter Horse race or the two minutes of the Kentucky Derby. The horse-racing industry is in for a very long pull if it is to make any progress in reducing impairment on the backstretch or on the frontside.

Chapter 14

What If We Do Nothing?

This concluding chapter will pose a number of questions, but it begins with a riddle: What if we do nothing? When you are doing nothing, you are doing something: you are doing nothing. Doing nothing is not an absence of activity: it is a decision, either conscious or unconscious, to maintain a status quo. In these dangerous times – dangerous for businesses, dangerous for the racing industry – standing still may be the first step to the graveyard. An axiom of business is that, if a company is standing still, it is falling behind. With that in mind, let us look at a few what-if type questions.

What if one day we woke up and, for whatever reason, all of the continent's race tracks were closed? The obvious result would be that there would be no racing.

Another hypothetical question: What if one day there were no owners or trainers available to enter their horses in races across the entire continent? Again, there would be no racing.

What if no jockeys showed up at the race tracks? Same result; there would be no racing.

If there were no racing in a state – because all race tracks closed or all owners and trainers suddenly disappeared, or whatever reason – would there still be a reason to have a state racing commission? Government moves in strange ways, but in times when less government is considered to be desirable, in all likelihood the racing commission would be abolished and the commissioners would lose their positions.

To be sure, these events are not going to happen – yet. The questions illustrate an important point, however. No matter how much trainers fight with the race track management or the track managers rail against the racing commissioners, or the trainers disparage the jockeys (or vice versa), their lives and their livelihoods are interconnected. They form a system, a system known as horse racing. Take away any one piece, and the system no longer functions. Of course, it is a peculiar system that all but prides itself on its disunity. For instance, when the Thoroughbred Racing Associations announced plans to create a commissioner – as the National Basketball Association has a commissioner and as the National Football League does as well – other racing organizations immediately took steps to name their own commissioners for racing. (Brian McGrath became the TRA's commissioner in 1994, but his function was primarily to develop new marketing initiatives for the Thoroughbred sport.) Among the larger groups within horse racing, the only one that most consistently speaks with a single voice is the American Quarter Horse Association, which has established an industrywide approach to substance-abuse programs.

As Hubbard Enterprises president Bruce Rimbo noted in his 1993 keynote address to the Conference on Alcohol and Drug Abuse Programs for the Horse Racing Industry, "we've always been slow to change. Lord knows this business does not move very quickly. We treated fans lousy for years. We've given them crummy food, unclean facilities. One thing we haven't given them for years was bad customer service, though, because basically we gave them no customer service. We had a monopoly. We opened the doors, and we stood behind the post because we didn't want to get overrun when they came roaring in the doors, and it worked for many years. Gosh, we were really brilliant." But at some point, probably beginning back in the 1960s or 1970s when more entertainment opportunities became available and the nation was wired for cable, race tracks began their long slide. In the mid-1990s, the race tracks found themselves in a struggle for survival – for the very existence of racing in some regions – against many new entertainment and gambling enterprises. They also find themselves staring face-to-face with a very sophisticated and determined competitor, the casino industry.

Determined competitors can be fatal when a company makes a conscious decision to maintain the status quo in the face of serious challenges, or if the company moves away from its strengths to mimic the competitor. And, for those within the industry who believe that racing will hang on long enough for them to grab a pension and retire from the field of battle, the deaths can come relatively quickly.

Examples abound in business, and one of the co-authors experienced a textbook case in Philadelphia several years ago. When the co-author went to work for the Philadelphia Inquirer in 1971, the Philadelphia Bulletin was the city's dominant daily newspaper. It was gray and boring, but it was rock solid, and it served the Main Line suburbs well. In 1970, however, a skilled and well-managed company, Knight Newspapers (later Knight-Ridder), bought the Inquirer, invested in excellence and created one of America's best newspapers under executive editor Gene Roberts. By 1983, the Philadelphia Bulletin was closed, overwhelmed by a determined competitor that aggressively peddled its excellence. When the Bulletin's management realized that the tide of battle had changed, it abandoned the things that it did best, which was serving as a reliable and largely accurate source of city and regional news, and hastened its demise. If anyone within the racing industry can see any parallels, they are welcome to them.

Rimbo, who initiated customer service projects at Hollywood Park and at tracks owned by Hollywood chairman R. D. Hubbard's Hubbard Enterprises, noted at the 1993 Louisville Conference that race tracks are trying to provide better customer service, and some are succeeding. Some tracks are also making investments in their backstretch stable areas, but usually that investment is concentrated on the barns rather than the living areas for the stable employees. After all, the people on the backstretch who are empowered – the trainers – are interested in their working conditions and the conditions in which their horses are maintained. When the day is done, they leave the race track and go home. But the people who remain do not have a voice, much less any power, and their needs are largely ignored except when empowered voices, such as those of Jim Ryan and Sports Illustrated's Bill Nack, serve as their advocates. Even then, those individuals who articulate what their eyes clearly see often are dismissed as misguided sentimentalists or as unenlightened about how things really are. Put another way, they are regarded as do-gooders, and stupid, too. But they are not; they are people of courage who have dared to call a spade a spade and to declare that this much-beloved sport – with its beautiful horses and bright colors and pageantry – is not really very pretty at all when the veneer-thin facade is stripped away.

With open eyes, anyone can see how deplorable the living conditions on America's race-track backstretches are. "I'm not a doctor of psychology or a doctor of anything, but you don't have to be a mental giant to see that the horrible living conditions on the backstretch lead to boredom and despair. Many end up in the substance-abuse program or need to be in it," said Joe M. Smreker at the Louisville Conference in 1991, when he was chairman of the Arkansas Racing Commission and the Association of Racing Commissioners International. "These conditions that exist are the fault of everyone in the industry: racing commissions, track management, and horsemen. It is up to all of us to get involved and do something for the program."

As much as any, that statement encapsulates the message of this entire work. Racing's components have been quick to point a finger at someone else as being responsible for combating substance abuse, but in truth everyone is responsible. While no entity is entirely responsible for rampant alcoholism and drug abuse on North America's race tracks, every component entity shares a responsibility for cleaning it up.

The National Football League and the National Basketball Association, the success stories of sports from the 1970s through the 1990s, have substance-abuse programs in place. Does racing? As a sport, no, although individual jurisdictions have undertaken to provide drug and alcohol counseling and treatment services.

Gerald Lawrence, who left Churchill Downs in 1990 and served as executive vice president of the New York Racing Association from January 1991 to August 1994, said in 1992 that theresponsibility extended beyond substance-abuse programs. "What we discovered is that what we really need is an involvement in the overall quality of life in the backstretch. What we really need to do at our race track – and you at your race tracks – is that we have to provide the people who live within the fences of our backstretches the same opportunities, the same quality of life that people who live outside our fences are entitled to. In a way almost, we've begun to feel that our people are not full citizens. They weren't getting all the services and all the help and all the aids that the people who weren't in racing were afforded because they lived in a community."

Each racing entity also has a responsibility to itself. Because, no matter how much some people may dispute the notion, investments in drug and alcohol programs find their way to the bottom line. Rear Admiral Paul Mulloy, U.S. Navy retired, estimated that one company, Owens-Corning, received a payback of $9 for every dollar it spent on treatment. In an economy where substance abuse is costing the national economy $200 billion a year, mostly in lost productivity, the payback on a clean and shaped up backstretch work force could be enormous. The question comes down to this: with so many potential benefits, why does the sport tolerate addiction rates above 35 percent at some race tracks? Why?

The horsemen owe it to themselves to develop a clean and reliable work force. They are paying every day in absences and oversights by impaired employees, and rising costs are pushing owners out of racing. For them, the up-front investment would be the smallest, and the payback undoubtedly would be the largest. An unimpaired work force is certainly the fastest and least expensive way to solve the "help problem" that everyone complains about on the backside.

How about the racing commissioners? They appear to have the least direct contact with the problem, but at the same time they have a very significant association because they license everybody. The commissioners grant racing dates and therefore effectively license the race track to conduct an enterprise, gambling, that otherwise would be illegal. They license an employee to work within the industry, and with that goes an implicit duty to assure that the environment in which they will be working is fit for human habitation. They also have a duty to the public to assure that the otherwise-illegal activity is being conducted in an acceptable environment, where the game is conducted fairly and where people are not asked to live in conditions that would make even the most hardened housing inspector wince.

"I think we as commissioners have more of a responsibility than just taking fingerprints and collecting money," said Russell Jones Jr., a well-known horseman and a Pennsylvania Horse Racing Commission member. "I think we have a responsible citizen's role in fostering something that will be an improvement for the entire industry."

In fact, every facet of the racing industry can make its contribution. For instance:

The race track could – and should – support on-track substance-abuse programs and provide safe and sanitary living conditions for workers housed on its property.

The racing commissions could – and should – institute the Berube Plan, articulated in 1991 by Paul Berube, the Thoroughbred Racing Protective Bureau's president. Under the Berube Plan, all new licensees would be required to complete an orientation program that includes the traditions of the race track, the conditions and expectations of regulators or race track security officers, and an introduction to the on-track substance-abuse program. The regulators also could state clearly and definitively that abusers will not be granted licenses. The licensing, for example, could be provisional pending a urine specimen and Breathalyzer testing.

Trainers could – and should – institute a drug-free workplace in their shedrows. They owe it to their unimpaired workers, they owe it to their horses, they owe it to their owners, and they owe it to themselves. Owners could – and should – insist that their horses be maintained in an unimpaired environment.

Surely, some cynics will dismiss such a program as impractical. They will say that it will cost money, which it will. But their statement – in some quarters, it would be regarded as poor-mouthing – ignores the fact that they are already paying a much higher cost for the abuse, and they will actually be saving money by investing in an unimpaired race track. Others will say, with perhaps even greater cynicism, that such a program will never root out substance abuse. To be sure, the problem is huge – "Everybody's drinking back there," one counselor observed – but not insurmountable. Admiral Mulloy noted that the substance-abuse rate in the Navy was almost 50 percent before he was put in charge of developing a substance-abuse program. After his retirement, in the early 1990s, the rate had fallen below 3 percent. And the benefits keep accruing. Mulloy estimated that the payback rate from the Navy's investment was $12 for every dollar put into treatment.

Admiral Mulloy also noted that substance abuse is not a backstretch problem so much as it is a leadership problem. So, too, did Tom Meeker at the 1990 Louisville Conference. "We need top-level management in our industry to say one thing, and that is we will support programs to assist folks who have problems," Churchill Downs's president said. "It's got to take the management and horsemen. I mean you have to go square eyeball to eyeball and look at these horsemen and say, do you want to piss away money – forgive my French – by letting people work in your barn who are not capable of treating and tending to your horses, who are going to cause you problems financially because that horse is going to go on the race track not properly bandaged, not cooled out once he comes back from the race track? Or do you want to have a quality work force – dedicated, loyal employees – who are going to treat your horses like no other group of employees are going to treat them, and make sure that when you and your partners send a horse to the race track, that horse is competitive? Now, that's what you've got to do."

Leadership has been spotty, at best, since the on-track counseling programs were launched in the mid-1980s. The American Quarter Horse Association has been highly supportive of the effort, and during its brief existence the American Horse Racing Federation, an American Horse Council branch headed by James Heffernan, also lent strong support to the Louisville Conference and other initiatives. The Thoroughbred industry has been less supportive, although individuals such as the Thoroughbred Racing Associations' Christopher Scherf, Jockeys' Guild National Manager John Giovanni, and John Hamilton, then with the Thoroughbred Owners and Breeders Association, participated actively in the Louisville Conference. Some show-world elements, such as the American Saddlebred Horse Association, in the person of its president Rondi Wightman, became involved in the Louisville Conference.

The Standardbred industry, in a sublime display of self-delusion, participated in the conference rarely and never embraced its work. One can only presume that harness racing believes it does not have any problems with alcohol and drugs.

In 1990, Meeker noted that the racing industry's leaders were missing from the conference, and he tried to change that for 1991, but his efforts were largely unsuccessful. Each conference offered a wealth of information and insight, but an overwhelming majority of race track managers concluded that they did not need to attend the conferences personally. Perhaps that was so. However, they certainly did need a high-level surrogate there to gather information and to develop contacts with others in the industry who were addressing the problems. Also, industry leaders needed the conference, or some means, for becoming aware of substance abuse because the welfare of their employees is of vital financial importance to them. After all, only top management can do the two things that are essential: identify the problem, and do something about it.

At the 1991 Louisville Conference, a former racing industry executive provided a management model taken from his current employer, McCormick & Co., the Baltimore spice maker. William L. Ramsey served as the TRPB agent at the Baltimore-area tracks and as director of operations at Pimlico Race Course before becoming director of safety, security, and services for McCormick in the late 1980s.

McCormick operates under a philosophy known as total quality management, and its keystone is training of its employees – all employees, both new hires and long-time workers, factory-level people and executives. Total quality management, Ramsey said, "it's a philosophy; it's a program; it's a way of life. It has to be all of those things to work; and what it means is that for 100 percent of the time, we strive to please our customer. Our customer is everybody. Our customer is the person we work next to. It's the person who rings the phone up and gives us an order. Our customer is everybody that we associate with in our professional life. That's our customer, and we treat everybody that way. So we strive to give them an accurate product, try to strive to give them what they want. We strive to give it to them on time, and we strive to do that every time. That is what total quality really means to a company."

The payback, he said, has been substantial. "It's allowed us to provide a better product, better service to our customers. Our business has grown immensely since we started our program. We've been able to document a number of instances where we've saved hundreds of thousands and even millions of dollars with good, total-quality ideas. And where do these ideas come from? And this is what we're talking about now. These ideas come from our employees because one of the provisions of total quality is that we must empower our employees to make these decisions. Total quality means that autocratic management can't exist in the total quality environment, that the employees must be empowered to make the changes, to change their environment, to make your business better."

That empowerment is achieved, in part, by training the employees – just as the Berube Plan seeks to involve new race-track employees in a positive work experience by training them in some basics as they come through the stable gate for the first times. McCormick teaches its employees about substance abuse, both its consequences and opportunities for help; racing should do no less.

The training also must extend to the horsemen, many of whom grew up in the backstretch culture and, in the turmoil of creating and maintaining a business, never have had an opportunity to learn about how much substance abuse is costing them. "The employer's the one who sees the problem first," said John Hamilton at the 1992 Louisville Conference. "The trainers need an awareness of their options when a problem occurs. That's the first thing, and they need to know how to detect the problem first, and they need an understanding of the recovery process."

Moreover, they need to understand the drug-free workplace concept and how they could institute one on their shedrows. Therein lies the big fear of horse people, and its corollary. The big fear is that, if they do not hire people who are impaired, they will not be able to find anyone at all to do the work. In fairness, this is not a cynical thought. Some trainers rationalize that they prefer an impaired but functioning groom or hotwalker to no groom or hotwalker at all. In the short term, that fear may have some validity. If a trainer refuses to hire someone because of substance-abuse concerns, he or she will not have that worker for that day. The employer is then faced with the choice of requiring existing employees to do the work and possibly driving them away, or doing the work himself or herself. But for every day thereafter, the trainer will have the negative effects of that worker's substance abuse. It is trading a short-term gain for a long-term pain.

Admiral Mulloy, in his 1991 presentation, provided an example from the world outside the stable gates that demonstrated the benefits of a drug-free workplace. The company, a plumbing concern, had 250 employees and was paying $7,000 to train each new employee and had a 70 percent turnover on its new hires. The company's accident rate was high, and its worker's compensation costs were approximately $185,000 annually. Then the company's owner instituted a pre-employment drug-testing program – a policy followed by about 75 percent of Fortune 500 companies at that time. "The stuff is a good deterrent," Mulloy said. The turnover rate dropped to 12 percent, and the company saved approximately $180,000 on training costs, while its worker's comp cost plummeted to about $35,000. That was at least a $330,000 savings, not counting increased productivity. Now, the company's owner has "250 people standing outside wanting to come into his drug-free outfit. And what do you think his clients think when he can say, 'We're drug-free,' and he has his plumbers in their house? Not bad business," Mulloy said.

No, it is not bad business, and it helps the company – or any company, or any industry – to protect and enhance its reputation. And a company or industry with a good reputation will attract good workers. The solution to the "good help" problem on North America's backstretches is to attract and retain the people who want to work in the industry and want to do so without having to work beside those who are impaired by alcohol or drugs.

The people who make racing their lives and livelihoods deserve no less. Racing deserves no less. It is the rock-bottom survival issue. If racing does not take the necessary steps to protect the integrity of its work force – which means providing a decent wage in a clean, drug-free environment – then racing will surely crumble from within rather than falling to the assault of casinos and riverboats. The game will get very dirty very fast, and bettors will abandon it for an antiseptic tug on a one-armed bandit.

What if we do nothing? To quote the University of Louisville's Lyle Sussman from the 1990 Louisville Conference, "if you do nothing, it's business as usual. It's the accidents. It's the injuries. It's the absenteeism. It's the turnover. It's the drug dealing and the other problems that you have on the backstretch at every track in the country. So at some point in time, you've got to break the cycle, and that comes from top leadership," he said. " It's as simple as that."

What if we do nothing? The result will be . . . nothing, an industry eaten alive by the cancer within it.

Chapter 15

Epilogue

In the preceding chapters, we have told the compelling, real-life stories that emerged from the five Conferences on Alcohol and Drug Abuse Programs for the Horse Racing Industry held in Louisville, from 1989 through 1993. The story has been told, for the most part, in the words of its participants.

Now, it is time to talk about what happened after the five Louisville Conferences. We begin by reviewing the importance of the American Horse Council's decision to establish the American Horse Racing Federation and its decision, in early 1994, to abolish that federation. It was the American Horse Racing Federation (AHRF), under the leadership of James Heffernan and the late R. Richards Rolapp, that brought leaders of the horse racing industry together to address the problems of alcoholism and drug abuse. In a sense, the AHRF Substance Abuse Committee served to salve some of the hurt feelings and rancor that accompanied the Ryan Family Foundation's matching-grant initiatives of 1989 and 1990. Represented on the Substance Abuse Committee were the Jockey Club (from which Ryan had resigned in protest), the Association of Racing Commissioners International (ARCI), the Thoroughbred Racing Associations (TRA), the Thoroughbred Owners and Breeders Association (TOBA), the American Association of Equine Practitioners, the Harness Horsemen's Association, the American Quarter Horse Association (AQHA), and the Jockeys' Guild. The first chair of the committee was HBPA President Mike Steele, who resigned for personal reasons before the committee's first meeting. Steele was succeeded by John Giovanni, national manager of the Jockeys' Guild, who remained as chairman until the AHRF's demise. Giovanni was assisted by the steady hand of Jim Heffernan, executive director of the AHRF.

Above all, the AHRF Substance Abuse Committee gave legitimacy to the effort to deal with alcoholism, substance abuse, and other human resources issues in the industry on an industry-wide scale. With the prestige of the organizations represented on the committee, and the unquestioned integrity of the late Rich Rolapp and the American Horse Council behind the effort, it was all but insulated from suggestions that the committee was self-serving or power-seeking. Organizations such as the Thoroughbred Racing Protective Bureau, the New York Racing Association, and the Race Track Chaplaincy of America also joined in and contributed to the committee's work. ARCI's Uniform Rules Committee used the Louisville Conferences to develop and test out its proposed regulations. Media representatives consistently covered the Louisville conferences and seemed to sense that something unusual was happening in the industry. Between conferences, one could find consciousness-raising articles about substance-abuse treatment and the drug-free workplace in publications such as Backstretch Magazine. Speakers for the annual conferences, while never easy to obtain, usually responded when called upon by their favorite racing organization's executive director or president. Thus, the list of speakers at the Louisville conferences is really a "who's who" of North American horse racing. Unfortunately, after just three years, the handwriting was on the wall and the AHRF's days became numbered. One factor, undoubtedly, was the failure of the major horsemen's group in the AHRF to pay its annual dues. This put severe financial pressure on the AHRF and, at the same time, seemed to prove, to those who already wanted to believe it, that organizations in horse racing would never be able to develop a common interest and work together to achieve it. The oft-heard adage was: "If the horse racing industry ever assembles a firing squad, it will stand them in a circle." By early 1994, the AHRF was no more. The American Horse Council chose not to continue on its own the work of the AHRF Substance Abuse Committee.

Anticipating the demise of the AHRF Substance Abuse Committee, one of the authors made a "modest proposal" at the 1993 Louisville Conference. He suggested that an organization to be called the Winners Federation be established to bring together the organizations that had formed the AHRF, the on-track substance abuse programs still existing in the industry, and other interested parties, such as the University of Arizona and the University of Louisville, United Professional Horseman's Association, and United Thoroughbred Trainers Association. Within the proposed federation, members of the Winners Federation would remain independent and autonomous but would be joined by common interests.

Dan Fick, director of racing for the American Quarter Horse Association, grasped the importance of the Winners Federation and took the lead in facilitating its development. In January 1994, a diverse group gathered in the Dallas-Fort Worth area to found the new organization.

The first specific task of the Winners Federation, the group decided, was to continue the annual conferences that had become the focal point of the industry's efforts to deal with human resources problems, including alcohol and drug abuse. To highlight the federation's role in fostering new programs, the 1994 conference was planned for New Mexico, the first state to establish a substance abuse program after the Ryan Family Foundation's grants for that purpose had concluded. Also, the federation established that its interim meeting would be held each year, in conjunction with the annual conference of the Association of Racing Commissioners International (ARCI). The first of these meetings was held in spring 1994, in Las Vegas. Problems of funding and leadership dominated the discussions at that time.

In October 1994, the Winners Federation conference was held successfully in Santa Fe, with the New Mexico Winners Circle Foundation carrying most of the load. Attendance was sparse when compared with previous conferences, and the emphasis was much more on clinical matters than had been the case in the past. The highpoint of the conference, however, was the keynote presentation by Ralph Scurfield, chairman of the California Horse Racing Board. Scurfield's thesis was that drug and alcohol problems placed the public's trust of horse racing at stake. Saying, "It's everybody's problem," Scurfield urged that the message:

" . . . echo off the San Gabriel Mountains at Santa Anita . . . the hill-top at Pimlico . . . the spires of Churchill Downs . . . and throughout the backstretches of Belmont Park, Hialeah, Ruidoso Downs, Turf Paradise, Louisiana Downs, Woodbine, and all of the other racetracks in North America because, folks, a lot of people haven't heard us yet or they are ignoring us."

Scurfield went on to cite "industry complacency" as the hardest obstacle to be overcome. Later, to the delight of all in attendance, Scurfield agreed to be the Winners Federation's first president.

Shortly thereafter, this excitement was dampened somewhat by the resignation, for personal reasons, of the federation's acting executive director, Rick Smith, who had served as president of California's Winners Foundation. Vice president Peggy Goetsch, of Illinois, stepped into this breach and has acted as de facto executive director since that time. Despite its many difficulties and setbacks, in 1997 the Winners Federation stands as an incorporated entity with 501 (c) (3) status expected to be awarded any day.

Soon, it became obvious to all that the Winners Federation could not achieve its goals without some equivalent of the American Horse Racing Federation Substance Abuse Committee's membership. One needed only to look around the table at the organization's meetings and notice who was not present. Racing's leaders were missing, again. It was as though all the good words of the five Louisville Conferences had never been said.

In 1995 and in 1996, the Winners Federation continued to hold vastly scaled-down conferences. The 1995 conference, held in New Orleans, attracted an outstanding keynote speaker, ESPN's Chris Lincoln, but registration did not warrant holding the conference. A better result was attained in 1996 when the Federation held a one-day conference just before the annual Race Track Industry Program symposium at the University of Arizona in Tucson. Still, the conference was but a shell of its former self, the Louisville Conferences.

The Winners Federation clearly needed a sponsor. It was decided that, despite its well-publicized problems, the Association of Racing Commissioners International (ARCI), before which Jim Ryan had announced his planned initiative, was the logical sponsor for the federation. ARCI President Tony Chamblin and officers who were in line to succeed as ARCI chairpersons were approached with the suggestion in late 1996. Initially, the response was positive but, as always, no definitive commitment had been made in the first quarter of 1997.

PERSPECTIVE

The alcohol and drug abuse programs that were established or augmented by funds from the Ryan Family Foundation were designed to help afflicted individuals and those whose lives were influenced by those afflicted individuals. This point must not be forgotten in evaluating what has occurred in the past decade and what may happen in the future if the Winners Federation or an equivalent organization becomes successful. The programs were not designed to eliminate drug and alcohol problems from the racetrack.

The reason for this is simple. There are ample officers of race track management, commissioners of racing, officers of horsemen's organizations, and security organization directors already who are responsible for the race track's environment. On one track that the authors know rather well, one can find, in a given week, representatives or officers employed by racing commission security, race track security, Thoroughbred Racing Protective Bureau, city police, county police, state police, joint police task force on drug enforcement, Drug Enforcement Agency, Federal Bureau of Investigation, and the Secret Service (provided that a protected official is visiting the track.) Surely, that much law enforcement resource could eliminate drug traffic on the backstretch if the decision were made to do it. Surely, pre-employment drug testing and addiction-related interviews could be conducted if these were demanded by backstretch employers, principally trainers. Surely, an industry that can afford a czar with a million-dollar price tag and a marketing program costing many more millions of dollars could establish a drug-free workplace. Surely, regulators in at least one racing state could declare their racetracks to be off- limits to those who deal drugs, to those who use illegal drugs, and to those who use legal drugs illegally or to excess. Instead, as former Backstretch Magazine editor Harriet Dalley said so poignantly at the 1992 Conference on Alcohol and Drug Abuse Programs for the Horse Racing Industry, the industry continues to lose the battle "one drug at a time, one drink at a time, and one person at a time."

IN CONCLUSION

And so we come to the end of our story. We conclude that no sport, and certainly no gaming opportunity, rivals the tradition, excitement, challenge, and beauty of horse racing. Early morning on the backstretch and an afternoon in the grandstand alike match some of the very best in the human experience. Racing's human resources, similarly, match the very best in skills, courage, knowledge, dedication, and humanity. There is love: love of sport, love of the equine athlete, love of each other. There is competition, fierce competition: hard fought and fair. Precious these are – too precious to be darkened by the tragedy of addictions that afflict those who would be winners.